THE DIVER'S WATCH

No other watch is engineered quite like a Rolex. The Submariner, introduced in 1953, was the first watch to be water resistant up to 100 metres. It was later strengthened by its patented triple-seal Triplock winding crown, making it capable of withstanding depths of up to 300 metres. The new 40 mm Submariner is presented here in 904L steel with a green Cerachrom disc.

THE SUBMARINER

Whatever you're saving for, we're here to help you on your journey.

From binoculars to balloon trips, over the last year we've helped more than seven million people save for what really matters to them.

To see how we can help you, come in and see us or visit lloydstsb.com/forthejourney

Lloyds TSB | for the journey...

Golden-cheeked Warbler *(Dendroica chrysoparia)*
Size: Head and body length, approx. 12 cm **Weight:** 8.7 - 12.1 g **Habitat:** Breeds only in the juniper-oak woodlands of central Texas; in non-breeding season, inhabits the Central American pine-oak forest region
Surviving number: Estimated at 9,600 - 32,000

Photographed by Gil Eckrich

WILDLIFE AS CANON SEES IT

Location, location, location. Only one place will do when it's time for the golden-cheeked warbler to breed: central Texas. This is where the beautiful bird locates Ashe juniper bark, which the female combines with feathers, grasses, leaves, mammal hair and spider webs to construct its open-cup nest. Males defend their breeding territory with song and chases, and will even attack invading males. They often return to the same site year after year, but they are finding fewer and fewer Ashe juniper trees standing when they do. As this vital raw material diminishes, so do the warbler's chances of building a life for the generations to follow.

As we see it, we can help make the world a better place. Raising awareness of endangered species is just one of the ways we at Canon are taking action—for the good of the planet we call home. Visit **canon.com/environment** to learn more.

NATIONAL GEOGRAPHIC

SEPTEMBER 2010 · VOL. 218 · NO. 3

34

On the Cover For its close-up,
King Tut's gold burial mask
was given a 90-minute reprieve
from its glass case at Cairo's
Egyptian Museum.
Photo by Kenneth Garrett

ngm.com DNA tests on
Egypt's royal mummies tell a
sometimes shocking tale. Our
interactive family tree sorts
out the incestuous relations
that were part of Tut's world.

FOR SUBSCRIPTIONS, GIFT MEMBERSHIPS,
OR CHANGES OF ADDRESS, CONTACT CUSTOMER
SERVICE AT *NGMSERVICE.COM,* OR CALL
1-800-NGS-LINE (647-5463). OUTSIDE THE U.S.
AND CANADA PLEASE CALL +1-813-979-6845.

BE A PART OF THE SOLUTION.

TAKE PART IN
The Great Energy Challenge

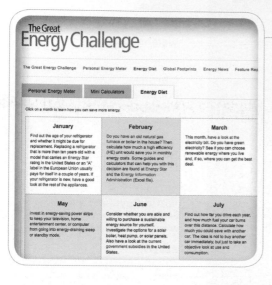

ENERGY DIET CALENDAR

Chock-full of ideas for conserving energy, this section helps you achieve your ideal "energy weight" by suggesting a month-by-month "diet" to help you get there.

ENERGY ACTION ATLAS

Use this map-driven online resource to find projects and initiatives around the world dealing with the vital energy challenges of our time. The Energy Action Atlas lets you be an advocate for a wide variety of cause-related activities by making a donation, volunteering, or just spreading the word.

ENERGY BLOG

Led by *nationalgeographic.com* Senior Editor Marianne Lavelle, the Energy Blog brings you the brightest ideas from some of the top minds leading today's energy conversation, including members of National Geographic's Energy Initiative Advisory Team.

NATIONAL GEOGRAPHIC

A NATIONAL GEOGRAPHIC INITIATIVE IN PARTNERSHIP WITH SHELL

The Great Energy Challenge is an important three-year National Geographic initiative in partnership with Shell designed to help all of us better understand the breadth and depth of our current energy situation. By joining The Great Energy Challenge and visiting the comprehensive online hub, we all can make a positive difference and change how we think about and consume energy. Let's start now at **greatenergychallenge.com**.

ENERGY NEWS AND FEATURES

Stay on top of the latest energy and environment developments and news with these regular updates and features.

PERSONAL ENERGY METER

Use the online carbon footprint calculator to measure your energy consumption. A variety of mini-calculators will allow you to understand the impact of common household appliances also affecting your footprint. After measuring your carbon footprint, you can share your score with your friends and compare your footprint against state and country averages.

ENERGY QUIZZES

These short interactive features will surprise you with "who knew?" facts about energy, environmental conservation, saving money, and more.

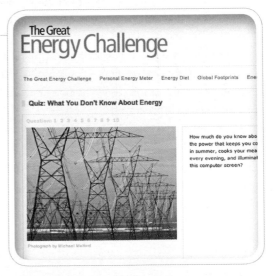

LEARN MORE TO DO MORE. START TODAY AT

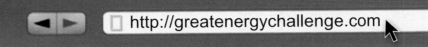

EDITOR'S NOTE

Shot from
Philippe Mathieu's
helicopter, rice
terraces surround
the village of Andina
in Madagascar.

As photographers in the field, we think we know the landscape.
Then we step into a helicopter, and suddenly the terrain unfurls before us. Philippe
Mathieu, the helicopter pilot who worked with Pascal Maitre on this month's
Madagascar story, was a photographer's dream. "He never said, 'I can't do this.'
It was always, 'Let's try,'" Pascal told me. Philippe knew how photographers think.
He understood about waiting hours for a few minutes of perfect light. With
Philippe's help, Pascal shot aerials of the Madagascar landscape and showed,
in ways that could never be comprehended from the ground, the scarification of
the land caused by mining and logging.

Philippe was a pro. But even the most careful pilot can be on the wrong side
of a set of statistics. On April 11, just weeks after Pascal had left Madagascar,
something went wrong—as yet no one knows what—and Philippe's chopper went
down. He was 38 years old.

His mother and sister were visiting him in Madagascar at the time. Afterward,
they waited for days to bring his coffin back to France, because ash from the
Iceland volcano canceled all flights. "With Philippe I never worried about anything
except the photographs," Pascal said. "We were a team."

COMING IN OCTOBER
The Gulf Oil Disaster Next month's
National Geographic will put the Gulf of Mexico
oil spill into context, providing an in-depth
analysis of oil exploration and its impact on the
ecosystem. A large, pullout map supplement will
take a comprehensive look at the Gulf region.
Working with dedicated people on the front lines
of the catastrophe, we'll tell a story that is both
timely and timeless. We'll use our expertise to
provide information and analysis you can trust.

Locks and ribbons at the Qingyin Monastery, Mt. Emei China.

Shot using the Samsung NX10 with 18-55mm lens set at 35mm, f/4.5, iso 400.

TYRONE TURNER

Tyrone Turner is a photojournalist based in Arlington, Virginia. His assignments have taken him from Brazil to Baghdad to the bayous of Louisiana with his camera in hand. In addition to his work for *National Geographic*, Turner has produced award-winning photographs for national and international publications such as *Time*, *Newsweek*, *U.S. News and World Report*, and the *Los Angeles Times*.

Unlocking the Secrets of a Great Shot

Of the four mountains considered holy by Chinese Buddhists, Mt. Emei is the largest. A green-clad giant that soars through the clouds in the middle of Sichuan Province, it holds 30 Buddhist temples on slopes rich with ancient trees, tumbling waterfalls and abundant wildlife. It is here that *National Geographic* photographer Tyrone Turner captured this shot that pleases the eye with its melange of light, texture and color, even as it teases the mind with its enigmatic subject matter.

Turner explains: "The locks and the ribbons are wishes. Pilgrims visit the monasteries on the mountain in order to pray and receive blessings. As well, people will buy these locks and ribbons for good luck and put them on the chain railings around the monastery ... they have brief sayings on them that represent their wishes."

As if having been granted his own wish, Turner says that the combination of overcast lighting conditions and my Samsung NX10 camera were ideal for the photograph. "I enjoyed the fact that the camera took really high-quality images in less than optimal lighting conditions," he said. Turner also commented that the size of the NX10 provided significant advantages over heavier gear: "The camera is light and small so it was easy to handle quickly in order to get the shot I wanted. Because the camera is small, it is less imposing to other people and so it was easy to be spontaneous while shooting."

NX10

www.samsung.com

www.samsungimaging.com

SAMSUNG

TURN ON TOMORROW

NATIONAL GEOGRAPHIC

Inspiring people to care about the planet

The National Geographic Society is chartered in Washington, D.C., as a nonprofit scientific and educational organization "for the increase and diffusion of geographic knowledge." Since 1888 the Society has supported more than 9,000 explorations and research projects, adding to knowledge of earth, sea, and sky.

THERE'S MORE TO LIFE THAN A VOLVO. THERE'S LOOKING GOOD AS YOU CRUISE PAST YET ANOTHER PETROL STATION. THAT'S WHY YOU DRIVE THE VOLVO C30 DRIVe

800 MILES BETWEEN FILL UPS*

At Volvo, we believe efficiency shouldn't compromise our unique style. That's why we created the C30 DRIVe, a car capable of 74.3mpg* and emissions of just 99g/km, giving you £0 road tax and Benefit in Kind from just £38†. So it looks as good on paper as it does on the road. For more information, call 0800 400 430 or visit www.volvocars.co.uk

Volvo. for life

LETTERS

May 2010

Mount St. Helens

Your update on Mount St. Helens's recovery heightened old memories. Shortly after the first eruption in 1980, a colleague and I flew along the skirts of the mountain, looking down on rows of huge, downed trees laid out in military order like so many toothpicks. Then came ranks of still standing trees: green on one side and the other, charred, facing the mountain. A year later, accompanying a group of forestry-school deans, we flew by helicopter into the crater, still steaming with the smell of brimstone. Yet on the nearby slopes the rejuvenation had begun. Spots of green were emerging from the ash, and files of elk made their way across the blackened landscape.

JAMES M. MONTGOMERY
Atlanta, Georgia

As European transportation remains crippled from the effects of the Eyjafjallajökull volcano, I commend you on your luck/foresight in having the May issue arrive at my house this week. Two hundred square miles of destroyed forest at Mount St. Helens is impressive, but a fourth day

(and counting) of a continent full of grounded air traffic seems equally so. I imagine that volcanoes, earthquakes, tsunamis, hurricanes, floods, and whatever else are not really more frequent than usual, but they do help us remember humility when we begin to get full of ourselves.

LONNIE HANAUER
West Orange, New Jersey

The most dramatic example of rebirth in the Mount St. Helens blast zone is seen on timber-company lands. By replanting their lands after the eruption in 1980, they now have a forest with 60-foot-tall trees. Wildlife and water quality also benefit from this active management.

ROD BARDELL
Lebanon, Oregon

Troubled Spirits

Perhaps some misguided or desperate people in Mexico call evil spirits "saints," but the author of "Troubled Spirits" must have known better. In the Catholic Church, saints are those who lived lives of virtue and piety and have been officially recognized by the church through canonization. They are held up as models of holiness, not idols to be worshipped. Surely they are not the cult figures described in your article. Please do not confuse saints and evil spirits. They are worlds apart.

JAN ALKIRE
Seattle, Washington

Your article successfully illustrated desperate people during a time of crisis. New controversial objects of prayer such as La Santa Muerte and Jesús Malverde simply tell us that humans suffering in

hopelessness and destitution turn to otherworldly figures for answers to the unanswerable. The same saints form the complexities of both the human and heavenly realms. As your article suggests, Mexico is not rife with inherently savage people, just complex ones living in troubled times.

MATTHEW HOLDMAN
Murray, Kentucky

Just as during Prohibition, so long as drugs are illegal in the United States, drug lords all over the world will continue to battle for turf because of the high profits caused by the illegality of drugs. No matter how hard we try to stop them, as the author states very perceptively, "with every new military offensive, the traffickers...became stronger." The war on drugs is Prohibition on steroids, causing literally tens of thousands of needless deaths and horrible misery. If we are concerned for the welfare of people, including our own children and their safety, we must end drug prohibition in America. Then the Mexican drug lords will suffer a fatal blow. Otherwise Mexicans will continue to worship La Santa Muerte, and for good reason.

JOHN DAVIS
Richardson, Texas

Corrections, Clarifications

May 2010: The Secrets of Sleep
Page 80: William Dement, dean of sleep studies at Stanford University, was incorrectly described as retired.

Email ngsforum@ngm.com
Write National Geographic Magazine, PO Box 98199, Washington, DC 20090-8199. Include name, address, and daytime telephone. Letters may be edited for clarity and length.

Smarter energy for a smarter planet.

For most of the last century, our electrical grids were a symbol of progress. The inexpensive, abundant power they brought changed the way the world worked – filling homes, streets, businesses, towns and cities with energy.

But today's electrical grids reflect a time when energy was cheap, their impact on the natural environment wasn't a priority and consumers weren't even part of the equation. Back then, the power system could be centralised, closely managed and supplied by a relatively small number of large power plants. It was designed to distribute power in one direction only – not to manage a dynamic global network of energy supply and demand.

As a result of inefficiencies in this system, the world's creation and distribution of electric power is now wasteful. With little or no intelligence to balance loads or monitor power flows, enough electricity is lost annually to power India, Germany and Canada for an entire year. In the UK, Government projections show that without new capacity generation, supply will not meet demand by 2016, whilst at the same time billions of pounds are wasted on energy that never reaches a single light bulb.

Fortunately, our energy can be made smart. It can be managed like the complex global system it is.

We can now instrument everything from the meter in the home to the turbines in the plants to the network itself. In fact, the intelligent utility system actually looks a lot more like the Internet than like a traditional grid. It can be linked to thousands of power sources – including climate-friendly ones, such as wind and tidal.

All of this instrumentation then generates new data, which advanced analytics can turn into insight, so that better decisions can be made in real time. Decisions by individuals and businesses on how they can consume more efficiently. Decisions by utility companies on how they can better manage delivery and balance loads. Decisions by governments and societies on how to preserve our environment. The whole system can become more efficient, reliable, adaptive... smart.

Smart grid projects are already helping consumers save 10% on their bills and are reducing peak demand by 15%. Imagine the potential savings when this is scaled to include enterprise, government departments and universities. And imagine the economic stimulus that an investment in smarter grids could provide in our current crisis.

In fact, there's no need for mere imagination. A recent report by the London School of Economics calculates that an investment of £5 billion in the development of a smart power grid in the UK could create or retain almost a quarter of a million jobs in energy and related industries. It could enable new forms of industrial innovation by creating exportable skills, resources and technology.

IBM scientists and industry experts are working on smart energy solutions around the world. We're working with utility companies globally to accelerate the adoption of smart grids to help make them more reliable and give customers better usage information. We're working on seven of the world's ten largest automated meter management projects. We're even exploring how to harness intermittent wind power by turning millions of future electric vehicles into a distributed storage system.

Our electrical grids can be a symbol of progress again – if we imbue the entire system with intelligence. And we can. Let's build a smarter planet. Join us and see what others are thinking, at **ibm.com/think/uk**

Baby Pictures Let's face it, most young things are adorable, regardless of size, shape, or species. But taking a perfect picture of one can be tricky. Our advice: Look for kids in odd poses or places, *then* capture their cuteness. When you've got just the right shot, send it to us. Every month this page features two photographs: one chosen by our editors, one chosen by our readers via online voting. For more information, go to *ngm.com/yourshot*.

EDITORS' CHOICE

Mariajoseph Johnbasco Neyveli, India

In India, hanging saris can double as rockers for toddlers. Johnbasco, 48, was visiting his mentor in Pondicherry when he noticed the man's granddaughter asleep in this colorfully cascading crib.

Linda Drake San Luis Obispo, California

"I go to this area in Manitoba every year to catch the bears coming out of their dens," says Drake, 40. Near Wapusk National Park she observed this little one hanging out with its mother. "We nicknamed it 'Velcro Cub,'" she says.

READERS' CHOICE

There's something inside
ERIC J HENDERSON

#9 ANGELICA FROM SAXONY

GRAINS OF PARADISE FROM WEST AFRICA

BOMBAYSAPPHIRE.COM/INSIDE

There's something inside
The
BOMBAY SAPPHIRE

Barbados Several species of morning swimmers—human tourists, protected turtles, assorted fish—share the azure waters of Paynes Bay. Boat operators here feed fish-strip breakfasts to about 15 young hawksbill and green turtles.

United States Seen from a satellite, the 2,600-acre "boneyard"—a 64-year-old depot at Davis-Monthan Air Force Base, in Tucson, Arizona—looks like parchment lined with toy planes. The site stores some 4,000 aircraft.

SATELLITE IMAGE: GEOEYE

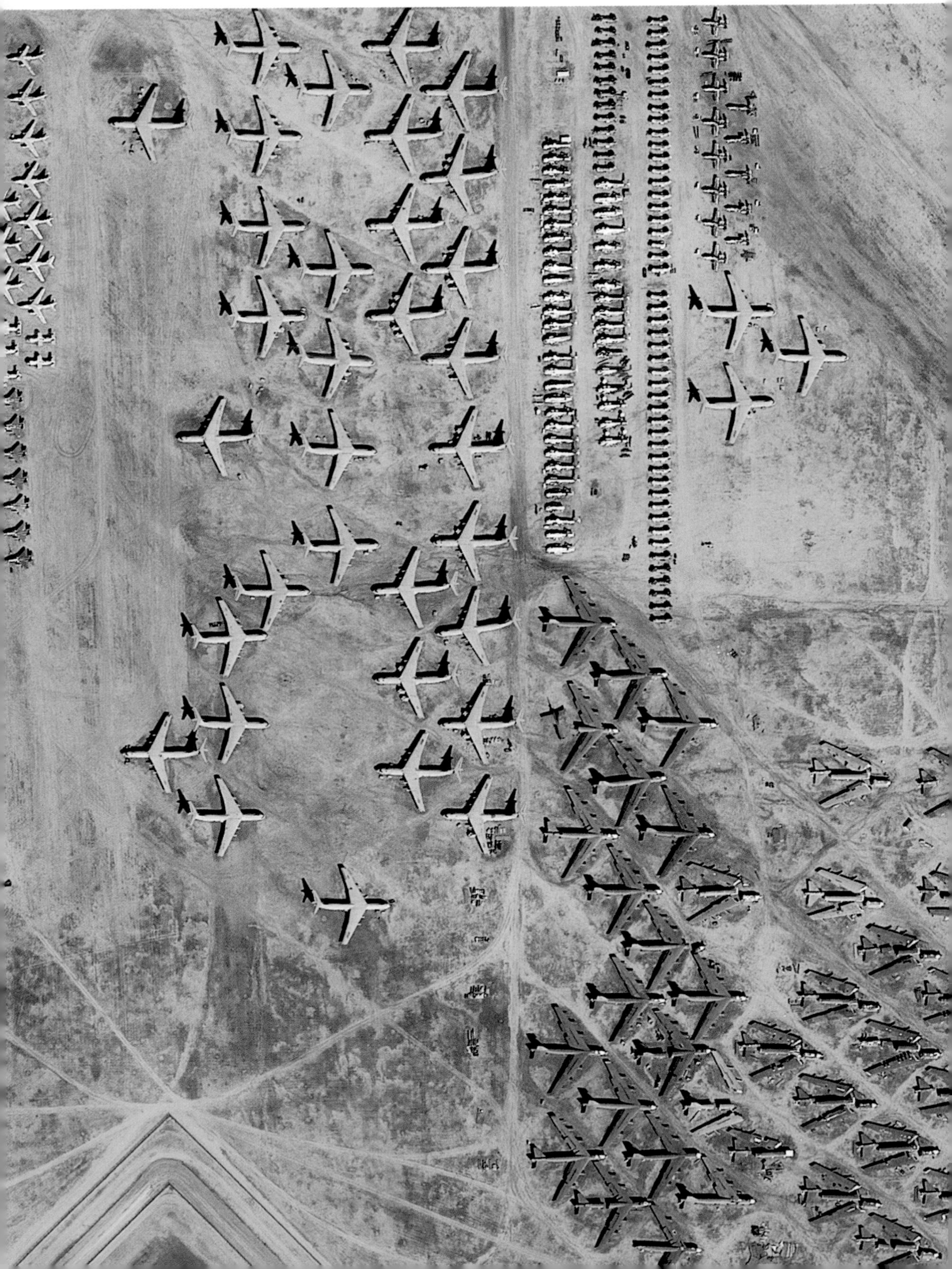

England Membranous wings spanning two feet and head tucked out of sight, an adult male Egyptian fruit bat negotiates netting in a London studio. This nocturnal fruit-eater was the living subject of an anatomical study.

➤ **Order prints** of *National Geographic* photos online at **PrintsNGS.com.**

Recovered artifacts bear witness to lives and buildings lost on September 11, 2001.

Found at Ground Zero

If every object tells a story, the ones displayed here speak of thousands with a common ending: a Georgia man whose wife slipped him a love note **1** for his trip to New York City; a woman with prayer beads **2** at work on the 98th floor of the World Trade Center; a husband who always carried a two-dollar bill **3** to remind him how lucky he was to have met his second wife.

Collected for the National September 11 Memorial & Museum, the objects tell of love, faith (Bible pages fused to metal **4**), lifestyles (a Mercedes key **5** and a golf ball **6**), and a workday (computer keyboard **7**) that came to a tragic end in 2001. The museum, set to open in September 2012, has some 3,000 artifacts so far, hundreds of them bestowed by relatives of those who perished.

A ladies' shoe **8** is one of several objects here that belong to survivors. The four-inch heels carried their owner down 62 floors, away from the crumbling south tower, and across the Manhattan Bridge to safety. —*Luna Shyr*

PHOTOS: IRA BLOCK
SOURCE: NATIONAL SEPTEMBER 11 MEMORIAL & MUSEUM

Reveal your natural talent
with the National Geographic
International Photography Contest

Islay presents many views to a photographer. The light and even the landscape seem to change from moment to moment, it is this environment that shapes the character of our perfectly balanced Bowmore Single Malt Whisky. With a passion for photography and with nature at our core, we invite you to capture moments at their finest.

We're delighted to partner with National Geographic UK in 2010 and are calling on you to get to the core of photography, by entering the International Photography Contest 2010. Send us your preferred photographs for your chance to feature in a future issue of National Geographic UK and to win a truly unforgettable trip to the home of Bowmore, Islay. To make even more of your photography, visit us online at Bowmore.com for hints and tips from expert photographers. Good luck, or as we would say in Scot's Gaelic - g'un rob h math agad.

VISIT NATIONALGEOGRAPHIC.COM/IPCUK2010 TO ENTER

INTERNATIONAL PHOTOGRAPHY CONTEST 2010   IN PARTNERSHIP WITH   BOWMORE ISLAY SINGLE MALT SCOTCH WHISKY

ISLAY TO THE CORE

VISIT BOWMORE.COM FOR MORE
drinkaware.co.uk for the facts

THE FIRST ISLAY SINGLE MALT WHISKY SINCE 1779

Cilantro is the leaf of the coriander plant. Detractors say even one small sprig tastes strongly of soap.

Herbaceous Debate

Cilantro is one polarizing herb. The seemingly innocuous staple of Mexican, Asian, and Indian cuisines has become a fresh ingredient in news stories and inspired passion-fueled blogs. Fans liken its notes to those of citrus; haters say they smack of soap. Whichever side of the produce aisle you're on, solidarity abounds.

Yet it isn't simply a matter of taste. According to Charles Wysocki of the Monell Chemical Sense Center, it's actually about flavor, which the brain perceives based on a complex combination of taste, smell, heat, texture. In the case of cilantro, Wysocki has a hunch that genes play a role too. His ongoing study of twins shows that identical ones have the same reaction to it far more often than fraternal ones do.

The genetic verdict is still out, but one thing is certain: In California, where annual records are carefully kept, cilantro production has doubled in the past decade. Agricultural economist Gary Lucier says Americans are eating on average at least a third of a pound of it a year, likely due to our increasingly diverse culinary scene.

Does that taste like victory, or work you into a lather? —*Catherine Barker*

I need Spain

* Mother Nature is wise. That's why she settled here.

Costs of Living
"Gain may be temporary and uncertain," Ben Franklin presciently said, but "expense is constant and certain." The current financial crisis has pared the wealth of developed nations, but housing, food, and clothing remain the staples of spending patterns everywhere. In 2009 households in rich countries spent proportionately less on such vitals than their counterparts in emerging or developing states.

Today economists are keeping an eye on young markets like China, where savings rates run high and spending is likely to increase as wages rise and growth leans less on exports. They're also looking at the fast-growing category of communications. "Mobile phones," says U.K.-based market analyst Media Eghbal, "are now driving spending and becoming 'essential' items." By 2020 they could be ubiquitous—meaning time, at least, may be spent the same everywhere. —*Jeremy Berlin*

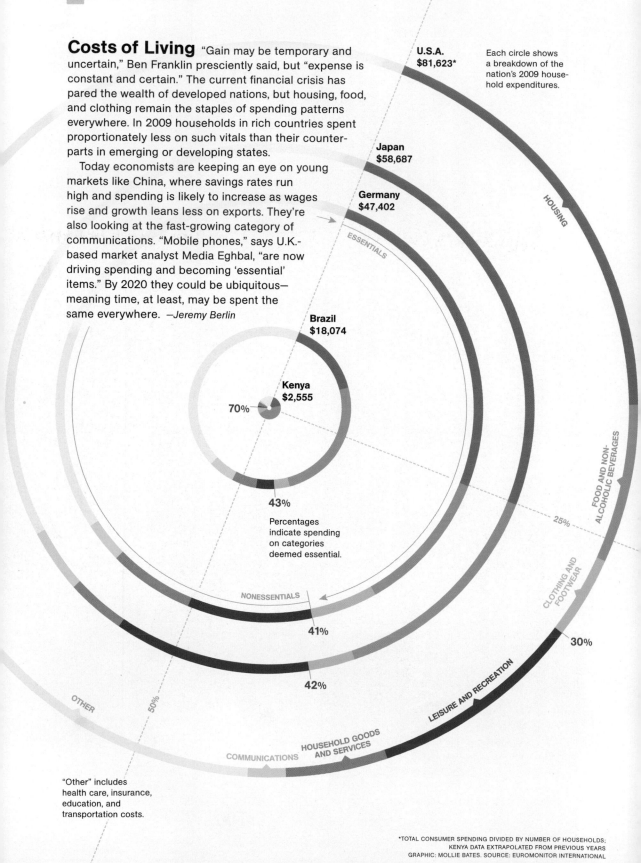

Each circle shows a breakdown of the nation's 2009 household expenditures.

U.S.A. $81,623*
Japan $58,687
Germany $47,402
Brazil $18,074
Kenya $2,555

ESSENTIALS

HOUSING

FOOD AND NON-ALCOHOLIC BEVERAGES

CLOTHING AND FOOTWEAR

LEISURE AND RECREATION

HOUSEHOLD GOODS AND SERVICES

COMMUNICATIONS

OTHER

NONESSENTIALS

70%
43%
41%
42%
30%
25%
50%

Percentages indicate spending on categories deemed essential.

"Other" includes health care, insurance, education, and transportation costs.

*TOTAL CONSUMER SPENDING DIVIDED BY NUMBER OF HOUSEHOLDS;
KENYA DATA EXTRAPOLATED FROM PREVIOUS YEARS
GRAPHIC: MOLLIE BATES. SOURCE: EUROMONITOR INTERNATIONAL

Portuguese Pioneers

Entering a new age of discovery

Portugal has always been famous as a nation of pioneers and inventors. It is over 500 years since Vasco da Gama sailed round the Cape of Good Hope, up the east Coast of Africa, and across the Indian Ocean to open up the spice trading routes that became the economic bedrock of Portuguese prosperity in the 16th century.

da Gama was only one in an illustrious line of Portuguese explorers who made their name on the back of royal patronage, advances in navigational technology – and the country's groundbreaking understanding and mastery of the Trade Winds that consistently buffet its Atlantic coast. It was the Portuguese who invented the *caravel* – the light sailing ship that facilitated exploration of the African coast by harnessing rather than fighting the elements.

Now Portugal is again in the vanguard of attempts to harness wind power – but this time for the purposes of tackling the global energy crisis. With wind projected to generate 30% of the country's electricity by the year 2020, the government has turned to the private sector to rekindle the drive and ingenuity that characterized the golden age of Portuguese commerce.

The market leader in the sector is Iberwind, whose 31 operational wind farms have a combined installed capacity of 680.75MW. Part of Iberwind's success lies in its excellent portfolio of wind farms located in the most attractive wind resource areas in Portugal, which consequently guarantee outstanding energy yields. This all conforms to the company's mission which, as President João Talone declares, is to "produce electricity using the wind as a clean and inexhaustible source."

As a result, Iberwind's annual turnover has reached €155m. The company's yearly production currently stands at 1.7TWh, which is 21% of Portugal's wind energy production, 3% of its entire electricity consumption, and a saving of 1m tons in CO_2 emissions. Not bad for a company with only 76 employees. da Gama and Co would be so proud.

Iberwind
www.iberwind.com

The Intelligent Investor
Director: D. Woodward
Regional Director: S. Onal
Editorial Coordinator: A. Bos
For more information visit:
www.intelligentinvestor.co.uk

Photo: iStockPhoto.com

Photo: REN

REN is a key innovator in the management of Portugal's electrical infrastructure.

Photo: REN

REN operates the largest share of Portugal's LNG storage infrastructure.

Like an Icelandic volcano, the sovereign debt crisis that erupted into life earlier this year has thrown up an economic cloud that may disrupt normal service across Europe for quite some time to come. But every cloud has a silver lining, and in this case it is the dispassionate reappraisal of each economy's strengths and weaknesses that the crisis has set in motion – and with it the identification of those industries that can help put the affected countries back on an even footing.

Portugal's renewable energy sector undoubtedly falls into this category. In March, the Portuguese government unveiled its 2020 Energy Strategy. Its key objectives – to promote renewable energies and endogenous resources to create employment; to reduce dependency on external energy sources; and to tackle issues of sustainability and climate change – could not have been more in tune with the overall policies of austerity and greater self-sufficiency that the Portuguese authorities have embraced since then.

It is no accident that Portugal has one of the highest renewable energy targets (45%) in Europe, for it is naturally blessed with more than its fair share of the sun, wind, and waves that constitute the raw materials for renewable energy production. But while this is helping to attract inward investment, there is more to it than that. "We have a strong legal and regulatory framework," claims Secretary of State for

Energy and Innovation, Dr José Carlos das Dorres Zorrinho. "We are a country with people who adopt new technologies very easily; and we have a cluster of enterprises, universities, and international partnerships that are helping to create a vibrant environment in which to test and develop new technologies. Portugal is becoming a living lab for new energy models. We are trying to be pioneers and we are achieving good results in terms of sustainability, in terms of economic rationality, and in terms of building an alternative to the normal energy market," he continues.

Parts of Portugal do indeed look like a 'living lab.' It will soon be home to the world's largest solar power plant; the first ever commercial wave plant is already situated on its North Atlantic coast; and several wind farms are scattered among its southern hills and plains.

At the heart of the regulatory framework that Dr Zorrinho alludes to, and the organization largely responsible for coordinating the electricity flow from many of these new energy sources, is the electricity giant REN, which in 2007 was granted an exclusive 50-year concession for the transmission of electricity through the National Electricity Transmission Grid. With the exception of distribution, the rest of the Portuguese electricity system – generation, supply, and retail – has been opened up to competition as a means of encouraging the private sector to play its full part in Portugal's energy revolution. REN therefore has a key role to play in ensuring that the citizens of Portugal actually get to reap the benefits of this move to renewable energy.

Photo: iStockPhoto.com

"The Portuguese energy sector is undergoing deep changes," explains Rui Cartaxo, REN's CEO. "While it is increasingly exploring its renewable energy potential in terms of wind and hydro productions, there have also been developments in other areas such as biomass, urban waste, and solar and wave power. These are at an early stage but are also attracting interest from investors. One of the key challenges for REN is to integrate the renewable generation facilities in the Portuguese energy system in a secure and economically efficient way. Given their unpredictability, renewable sources pose specific challenges for electricity grids. This calls for smarter and more robust power grids in order to keep the system permanently balanced." Cartaxo continues, "Part of the solution for us is to have good cross-border interconnections with Spain, and these are currently being upgraded. We are also making sure that our electricity substations can cope with bidirectional power flows and more volatile power charge conditions across the grids."

As well as being Portugal's sole electricity transmitter, REN also owns and operates the lion's share of the country's natural gas infrastructure, including its high-pressure pipelines, its Liquefied Natural Gas (LNG) terminal, and most of its underground storage facilities. "There are three good reasons to have natural gas as a back-up to renewable energy," says Cartaxo. "Firstly, it is the cheapest and cleanest fossil resource for power generation. Second, gas-fired turbines are relatively cheap and

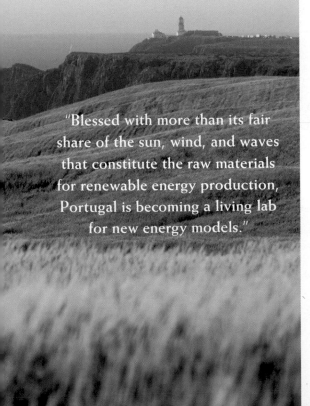

"Blessed with more than its fair share of the sun, wind, and waves that constitute the raw materials for renewable energy production, Portugal is becoming a living lab for new energy models."

fast to build, and allow for a flexible operation regime that is crucial to ensuring the balance of the energy systems when you have to compensate for variations in renewable source availability. Third," he continues, "natural gas can be stored, which again allows you to make provisions against shortages in renewable energy."

REN is set to play a vital part in helping its country weather the current economic storm, both by cutting the country's energy bill and by creating jobs – but also by exporting the expertise developed in the 'living lab.' The export initiative is being driven by companies such as the EDP Group, one of REN's shareholders: "Ten years ago EDP was a totally national company," says CEO Antonio Mexia. "Last year, only 52% of our revenues came from Portugal; by 2015 we will be a true multinational with offices in 26 US states as well as Bilbao, Bucharest, Paris, Sao Paolo, and Macau."

Just like the famous 15th-century sailors and navigators who boldly explored new territories, Portuguese pioneers are once again at the forefront of this brave new world of renewable energy as REN takes its experience and know-how overseas, through the supply of engineering and consultancy services to Austral Africa, Brazil, and beyond.

The spirit of Portugal's Age of Discovery is, it appears, alive and well.

Nutrition Facts
Giant water bugs
Serving size: 100g

Amount Per Serving

Calories 62
Total Fat 8.3g
Phosphorus 226mg
Iron 14mg
Calcium 44mg
Carbohydrate 2.1g
Protein 19.8g

Crawly Cuisine

Don't bug out, but the UN's Food and Agriculture Organization is working on a policy to promote insects as food worldwide. Turns out beetles, crickets, and many other types are rather nutritious. A serving of small grasshoppers, for instance, packs nearly the same protein punch as ground beef. And insects can be farmed more cheaply and on much less land. At least a thousand species are already part of the human diet: Mexicans liquefy stinkbugs for sauces, Thais deep-fry giant water bugs, and Australian Aborigines chew ants that have a lemony flavor.

As the global population nears seven billion, the FAO sees insect farming as a move toward food security—a subject for its upcoming conference on entomophagy, the practice of insect eating. Getting skittish diners in the West to swallow the idea poses the biggest challenge, says entomologist Gene DeFoliart, who has a penchant for termites. "It's time to take this seriously," he says. Once we do, a fly in your soup could come with the chef's compliments. —*Jennifer S. Holland*

Small grasshoppers Serving size: 100g	Red ant eggs Serving size: 100g	Crickets Serving size: 100g
Amount Per Serving	**Amount Per Serving**	**Amount Per Serving**
Calories 153	Calories 83	Calories 122
Total Fat 6.1g	Total Fat 3.2g	Total Fat 5.5g
Phosphorus 238mg	Phosphorus 113mg	Phosphorus 185mg
Iron 5mg	Iron 4mg	Iron 10mg
Calcium 35mg	Calcium 8mg	Calcium 76mg
Carbohydrate 3.9g	Carbohydrate 6.5g	Carbohydrate 5.1g
Protein 20.6g	Protein 7g	Protein 12.9g

PHOTOS: JOEL SARTORE; STEFAN SOLLFORS, ALAMY (ANT)
SOURCE: JULIETA RAMOS-ELORDUY, *CREEPY CRAWLY CUISINE*

An Explosive Wager

Never mind the World Cup or Super Bowl. With a bevy of volcanoes in various states of agitation, a Dublin bookie offers the chance to cash in on the ones that blow.

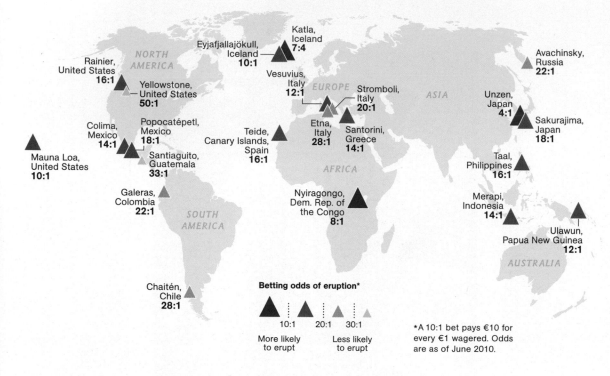

Katla, Iceland 7:4

Eyjafjallajökull, Iceland 10:1

Rainier, United States 16:1

Yellowstone, United States 50:1

Vesuvius, Italy 12:1

Stromboli, Italy 20:1

Avachinsky, Russia 22:1

Unzen, Japan 4:1

Colima, Mexico 14:1

Popocatépetl, Mexico 18:1

Teide, Canary Islands, Spain 16:1

Etna, Italy 28:1

Santorini, Greece 14:1

Sakurajima, Japan 18:1

Mauna Loa, United States 10:1

Santiaguito, Guatemala 33:1

Taal, Philippines 16:1

Galeras, Colombia 22:1

Nyiragongo, Dem. Rep. of the Congo 8:1

Merapi, Indonesia 14:1

Ulawun, Papua New Guinea 12:1

Chaitén, Chile 28:1

NORTH AMERICA · SOUTH AMERICA · EUROPE · ASIA · AFRICA · AUSTRALIA

Betting odds of eruption*

10:1   20:1   30:1

More likely to erupt   Less likely to erupt

*A 10:1 bet pays €10 for every €1 wagered. Odds are as of June 2010.

It's an investment even more volatile than stocks: the next big volcanic eruption. Well before Iceland's Eyjafjallajökull blew this year, Ireland's largest bookie, Paddy Power, was letting punters bet on the peak they deemed most likely to explode. The seven-to-four favorite? Another Icelandic peak, Katla. Eyjafjallajökull now sits in fourth place, along with Hawaii's Mauna Loa (ten to one). Unlikely to go off, but with a big purse if it does: Yellowstone (50 to one).

"Volcanoes with regular lava flows or burps are hot favorites," says Paddy Power spokesman Darren Haines. "Dormant volcanoes can see odds as low as 500 to one." Probabilities are calculated using the Volcanic Explosivity Index—the scale, ranging from zero (nonexplosive)

to eight (megacolossal), that scientists use to rank eruption severity. The first volcano to hit level three, with plumes at least two miles high, will prompt payouts.

Paddy Power's clients came up with the novel market after the 2009 eruption of the Philippines' Mount Mayon. If natural phenomena aren't your thing, this year's bets have also included the next Oscar winners, pope, and James Bond actor—and which country will make first contact with space aliens. (Ireland and the United States were top picks.) On a more somber note, one could have wagered on how many wild polar bears will exist as of the end of 2011 and how many species will be critically endangered. Here's hoping the odds land in the animals' favor.
—Jennifer S. Holland

Eyjafjallajökull volcano

EXPERT'S EYE
PEOPLE

PHOTO TIPS

- Know your subjects and never judge them. Empathy and emotion are key tools for a photographer.

- Don't shy away from the intimate moment. Be open to life as it happens.

- Faces emit character. Learn to read your subject's emotions and let each face tell its own story.

- The best gestures happen in a blur of motion. Keep shooting and you'll get the image you want.

- Life happens in dark places too: bring your camera out at night.

Jim Richardson composed this portrait at Harvest Festival in Cuba, Kansas, while lying on his back. "In this business," says the National Geographic veteran, "you can't be afraid of looking foolish." The unusual perspective made his subjects loom like colossi, their strained faces framed by the casual poses of towns-people and a line of facades.

Richardson felt comfortable in Cuba, having spent years getting to know the rhythms of the town. The Benyshek brothers were likewise at ease with the man shooting up into their faces as they struggled for local glory during the "People Pull" competition. "Believe me, if I'd distracted them," says Richardson, "I'd still be buying them beers."

Richardson believes people are complex subjects, demanding the empathy of the photographer and the patience to wait for the moment he calls "super-reality," when deeper truths and hidden dynamics behind a gesture are revealed. In this case, the town's never-say-die mentality was immortalized in a moment.

For more about Jim Richardson, see:

jimrichardsonphotography.com

Revealed World

Imagine bubbles floating before your eyes, filled with cool info about stuff you see on the street. Science fiction? Nope. It's augmented reality. And one day it'll be as routine as browsing the Web.

2009
Smart phone

2010
Eyewear

2015?
Contact lenses

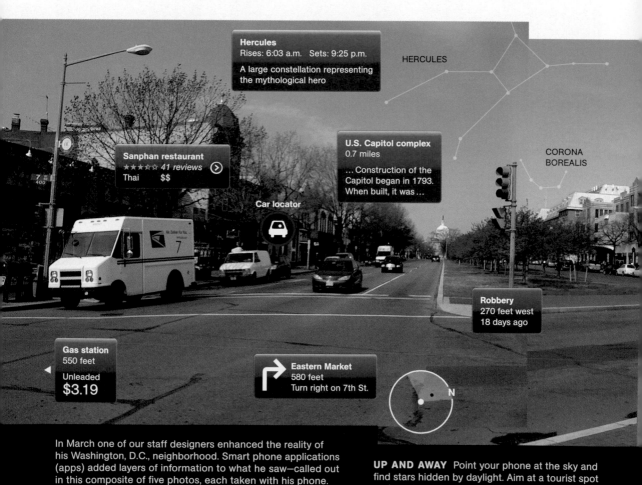

Hercules
Rises: 6:03 a.m. Sets: 9:25 p.m.
A large constellation representing the mythological hero

HERCULES

Sanphan restaurant
★★★☆☆ 41 reviews ⊙
Thai $$

U.S. Capitol complex
0.7 miles
... Construction of the Capitol began in 1793. When built, it was ...

CORONA BOREALIS

Car locator

Robbery
270 feet west
18 days ago

Gas station
550 feet
Unleaded
$3.19

Eastern Market
580 feet
Turn right on 7th St.

N

In March one of our staff designers enhanced the reality of his Washington, D.C., neighborhood. Smart phone applications (apps) added layers of information to what he saw—called out in this composite of five photos, each taken with his phone.

UP AND AWAY Point your phone at the sky and find stars hidden by daylight. Aim at a tourist spot and see its history plus info for visitors. For an augmented-reality check, tap into crime stats.

YOU COULD CALL IT REALITY 1.0—the unvarnished world presented to us by our five senses. It's not always the most user-friendly of places. We get lost in unfamiliar cities; we meet people whose language we don't understand. Fortunately there's an upgrade in the works that might eliminate some of the bugs: augmented reality, or AR. This emerging technology superimposes computer-generated images on the real world, courtesy of a cell phone camera or special video glasses.

Early forms of AR have already arrived. After downloading software, owners of smart phones like the iPhone and Droid can use the built-in GPS, compass, and camera to find information about nearby ATMs and restaurants, the closest subway stop, and other points of interest in some cities. With AR you might aim a phone's camera at a restaurant, and on the screen you'll see not just the venue but also a review hovering above it.

The U.S. Marine Corps is testing AR technology developed at Columbia University to train mechanics. They don headgear that projects animated 3-D computer graphics onto the equipment under repair, labeling parts and giving step-by-step guidance. "The marines worked faster with our AR program than with laptop-based manuals," says Steven Feiner, a computer scientist at Columbia.

Early adopters can test out the world's first augmented-reality glasses for consumers, *(Continued)*

622-624 North Carolina Ave. SE
900 feet
List price: **$2,995,000**
Bed: **7**   Bath: **8**
On market: **420 days**

flickr: Eastern Market Fire
510 feet
Taken: 2007-04-30
09:35:35 a.m.

Peregrine Espresso
195 feet
Free Wi-Fi

Bus stop
70 feet
Nearest for
32 34 36
A11 C40
CIRC

Twitter users in the area
perfect day to head to @EasternMarketDC anyone want to meet up? #spring #dc #market
Posted by @ARpro 10 minutes ago

Subway stop
140 feet
Nearest for
● Orange Line
● Blue Line

REAL DEALS Various apps can steer you to the cheapest gas around, mass-transit options, good food, and Wi-Fi spots. You can also learn the price of that town house that's up for sale.

STREET PALS The Tweeps Around app tells if tweeters are near. Flickr displays area photos by members (Eastern Market, above). In the works: an app to match faces to social-network profiles.

world beat

CATHAY PACIFIC AIRWAYS

"I was the new kid who nobody would talk to."

"When I was 17, my dad sent me to a posh school in New Jersey where there were only four other Asian kids. I was miserable, but I learned that life is all about believing in yourself and having confidence, and now I'm comfortable anywhere.

I fly between San Francisco and Hong Kong, but I really want to visit Santorini in Greece—a little island splashed with whitewashed houses above a blue, blue sea. I'd have a backpack. No makeup. No high heels…and if you meet me online, I'll tell you what else I'm packing."

Alice Wong, Flight Purser

Visit our Meet the Team website to meet Alice and a hundred more staff who always go the extra mile to make you feel special.

Great service. Great people. Great fares. Visit *cathaypacific.com*.

TAG HEUER AND TESLA

A unique pioneering partnership.

Avant-garde watchmaker TAG Heuer and electric car maker Tesla Motors have teamed up in a worldwide partnership as the iconic Swiss brand celebrates its 150th anniversary. This is to be marked by a World Tour featuring the 2010 TAG Heuer Tesla Roadster, set to visit 15 key cities. This one-of-a-kind collector's car boasts a unique interior incorporating TAG Heuer cutting-edge design elements with a specially designed center console containing the latest 2010 concept watch, the TAG Heuer Pendulum, the first ever mechanical movement without a hairspring. The car also features a TAG Heuer Meridiist mobile phone as well as a one-fifth second Heuer Limited Edition Stopwatch.

To find out more about this pioneering partnership and about the World Tour, please visit *www.odyssey.tagheuer.com*.

SUSTAINABLE TOURISM

The next big tourism growth market.

World Green Tourism Abu Dhabi is the much needed platform to identify commercial opportunities in this growing market and to prepare businesses during these changing times.

The conference, presented by the Abu Dhabi Tourism Authority, will take place November 22–24, 2010, at the Abu Dhabi National Exhibition Centre and will include a lineup of powerful speakers from the International Council for Responsible Tourism U.K., the National Geographic Center for Sustainable Destinations, Starwood Worldwide, and many more.

The supporting exhibition will bring together regional and international tourism authorities, urban city planners, hotels and resorts, property developers, airlines, tour operators, green products suppliers, museums, and heritage site organizations.

If you would like to take advantage of this unique opportunity, contact Rick Theobald at
T: +971 4 332 9029 or
E: rick@worldgreentourism.ae

OPEN PLANET *ideas*

A new online platform designed to tackle some of the world's most important environmental issues has been created by Sony in conjunction with WWF. Launching in September 2010, Open Planet Ideas is a social networking site intended to generate concepts for how technology can be repurposed and reapplied to tackle key environmental concerns.

This online community welcomes people interested in design, engineering, and sustainability as well as members of the public who will work together to develop concepts for more environmentally sustainable technology.

A vote will be held for a winning concept, and the team behind the winning idea will have the chance to work with Sony engineers and WWF specialists to bring the concept to life.

To become part of this innovative community or to find out more, please visit us at *www.openplanetideas.com*.

THE BIG IDEA

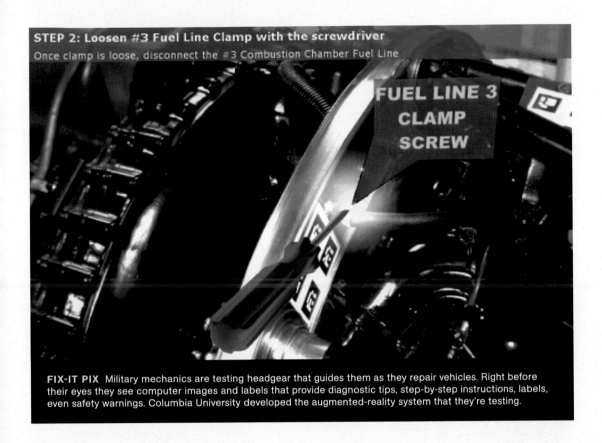

STEP 2: Loosen #3 Fuel Line Clamp with the screwdriver
Once clamp is loose, disconnect the #3 Combustion Chamber Fuel Line

FUEL LINE 3 CLAMP SCREW

FIX-IT PIX Military mechanics are testing headgear that guides them as they repair vehicles. Right before their eyes they see computer images and labels that provide diagnostic tips, step-by-step instructions, labels, even safety warnings. Columbia University developed the augmented-reality system that they're testing.

from a U.S. company called Vuzix. They look like wraparound sunglasses, except you can't see directly through the lenses. Instead, small cameras centered on the outside of each lens feed continuous video through a mobile computer (say, an iPhone) to an LCD screen mounted inside each lens. So you look at the world indirectly, through the two tiny cameras' feed. (And without a panoramic field of view, you'll have to be careful where you walk.) The price for the glasses with cameras is about $600.

When connected to an iPhone, an iPod, or a PC for at-home gaming, the glasses combine computer input with the live video, creating a single stereoscopic field of view on the LCD, where computer graphics merge with the real world. Paul Travers, president of Vuzix, says that in the near future video glasses will deliver spectacular AR effects. "Instead of a little cell phone display, you'll have an image on the LCD that looks like an IMAX theater filling your field of view."

The next stage in the evolution of AR is taking shape in the lab of Babak Parviz, an associate professor of bio-nanotechnology at Seattle's University of Washington. Parviz has made a contact lens etched with a tiny, transparent electronic circuit that contains a single LED. Over the next several years he hopes to add hundreds of LEDs to the lens, allowing it to display text and images that would appear to hover in space at a readable distance in front of the eye. "With enough processing power, the lens could translate speech into text in real time and display it for deaf people," says Parviz. The lens would be powered wirelessly by radio waves transmitted from a cell phone in your pocket.

But for many users, AR might add to the toll that distracting technologies take on personal interaction. Scott Rigby, founder of Immersyve, a research group that studies the psychological effects of video games, wonders: "What will the consequences be of immersing yourself in a world that is isolated from the person standing next to you?" Welcome to reality 2.0. *—Tim Folger*

KING TUT'S FAMILY SECRETS

DNA evidence reveals the truth
about the boy king's parents and new clues
to his untimely death.

A COFFIN OF SOLID GOLD WEIGHING ALMOST 250 POUNDS HELD THE KING'S MUMMIFIED REMAINS.

Icon of ancient Egypt, the teenage pharaoh's funerary mask immortalizes his features in gold, glass, and semiprecious stones. This and other treasures from his tomb, now in Cairo's Egyptian Museum, attract a constant swirl of visitors.

*Hidden in the desert canyons **west of the Nile**, the Valley of the Kings **holds** the **tombs of King Tut** and his royal relatives. **In antiquity this was** considered a secluded spot. **Today the growing** suburbs of Luxor shimmer nearby.*

By Zahi Hawass   Photographs by Kenneth Garrett

MUMMIES CAPTURE OUR IMAGINATIONS AND OUR HEARTS. FULL OF SECRETS AND MAGIC, THEY WERE ONCE PEOPLE WHO LIVED AND LOVED, JUST AS WE DO TODAY.

I believe we should honor these ancient dead and let them rest in peace.

There are some secrets of the pharaohs, however, that can be revealed only by studying their mummies. By carrying out CT scans of King Tutankhamun's mummy, we were able in 2005 to show that he did not die from a blow to the head, as many people believed. Our analysis revealed that a hole in the back of his skull had been made during the mummification process. The study also showed that Tutankhamun died when he was only 19—perhaps soon after he suffered a fracture to his left leg. But there are mysteries surrounding Tutankhamun that even a CT scanner cannot reveal. Now we have probed even deeper into his mummy and returned with extraordinary revelations about his life, his birth, and his death.

To me the story of Tutankhamun is like a play whose ending is still being written. The first act of the drama begins in about 1390 B.C., several decades before Tutankhamun's birth, when the great pharaoh Amenhotep III assumes the throne of Egypt. Controlling an empire stretching 1,200 miles from the Euphrates in the north to the Fourth Cataract of the Nile in the south, this king of the 18th dynasty is rich beyond imagining. Along with his powerful queen Tiye, Amenhotep III rules for 37 years, worshipping the gods of his ancestors, above all Amun, while his people prosper and vast wealth flows into the royal coffers from Egypt's foreign holdings.

If Act I is about tradition and stability, Act II is revolt. When Amenhotep III dies, he is succeeded by his second son, Amenhotep IV—a bizarre visionary who turns away from Amun and the other gods of the state pantheon and worships instead a single deity known as the Aten, the disk of the sun. In the fifth year of his reign, he changes his name to Akhenaten— "he who is beneficial to the Aten." He elevates himself to the status of a living god and abandons the traditional religious capital at Thebes, building a great ceremonial city 180 miles to the north, at a place now called Amarna. Here he lives with his great wife, the beautiful

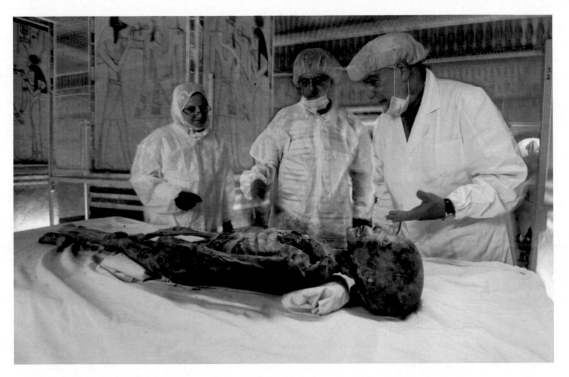

Nefertiti, and together they serve as the high priests of the Aten, assisted in their duties by their six cherished daughters. All power and wealth is stripped from the Amun priesthood, and the Aten reigns supreme. The art of this period is also infused with a revolutionary new naturalism; the pharaoh has himself depicted not with an idealized face and youthful, muscular body as were pharaohs before him, but as strangely effeminate, with a potbelly and a thick-lipped, elongated face.

The end of Akhenaten's reign is cloaked in confusion—a scene acted out behind closed curtains. One or possibly two kings rule for short periods of time, either alongside Akhenaten, after his death, or both. Like many other Egyptologists, I believe the first of these "kings" is actually Nefertiti. The second is a mysterious figure called Smenkhkare, about whom we know almost nothing.

What we know for sure is that when the curtain opens on Act III, the throne is occupied by a young boy: the nine-year-old Tutankhaten ("the living image of the Aten"). Within the first two years of his tenure on the throne, he and his wife, Ankhesenpaaten (a daughter of Akhenaten and Nefertiti), abandon Amarna and return to Thebes, reopening the temples and restoring their wealth and glory. They change their names to Tutankhamun and Ankhesenamun, proclaiming their rejection of Akhenaten's heresy and their renewed dedication to the cult of Amun.

Then the curtain falls. Ten years after ascending the throne, Tutankhamun is dead, leaving no heirs to succeed him. He is hastily buried in a small tomb, designed originally for a private person rather than a king. In a backlash against Akhenaten's heresy, his successors manage to delete from history nearly all traces of

GRAND-FATHER

Amenhotep III *KV35*

Now identified as Tut's grandfather, Amenhotep III
(below and at right) ruled in splendor some 3,400 years
ago. His mummy was buried with a wealth of goods.
Several hundred years later, priests seeking to protect
such royal remains from tomb robbers wrapped the
mummies in fresh linens and reburied them in groups.
Amenhotep III's body was found in 1898 hidden along
with more than a dozen other royals in KV35, the
tomb of his own grandfather, Amenhotep II.

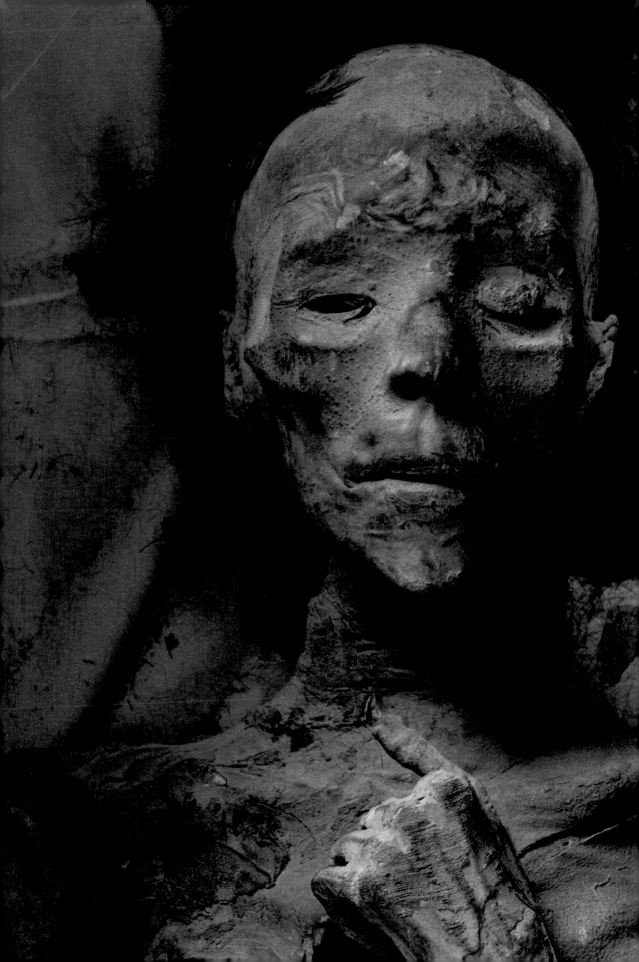

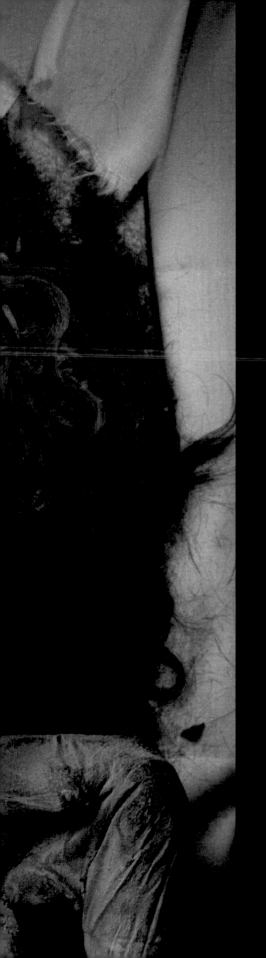

GRAND-MOTHER

Tiye *KV35EL*

Among the remains in the KV35 cache was
an unidentified mummy known until now only as the
Elder Lady. DNA has identified this regal beauty
as Amenhotep III's wife Tiye, the daughter of Yuya and
Tuyu, a nonroyal couple discovered in 1905 in their
own undisturbed tomb, KV46. The grandmother of Tut,
Tiye was embalmed with her left arm bent across her
chest—interpreted as a queen's burial pose.
Her statue from the temple at Karnak (below)
displays a similarly bent left arm.

the Amarna kings, including Tutankhamun.

Ironically, this attempt to erase his memory preserved Tutankhamun for all time. Less than a century after his death, the location of his tomb had been forgotten. Hidden from robbers by structures built directly above, it remained virtually untouched until its discovery in 1922. More than 5,000 artifacts were found inside

HIDDEN FROM ROBBERS, TUT'S TOMB REMAINED VIRTUALLY UNTOUCHED UNTIL ITS DISCOVERY IN 1922.

the tomb. But the archaeological record has so far failed to illuminate the young king's most intimate family relationships. Who were his mother and father? What became of his widow, Ankhesenamun? Are the two mummified fetuses found in his tomb King Tutankhamun's own prematurely born children, or tokens of purity to accompany him into the afterlife?

To answer these questions, we decided to analyze Tutankhamun's DNA, along with that of ten other mummies suspected to be members of his immediate family. In the past I had been against genetic studies of royal mummies. The chance of obtaining workable samples while avoiding contamination from modern DNA seemed too small to justify disturbing these sacred remains. But in 2008 several geneticists convinced me that the field had advanced far enough to give us a good chance of getting useful results. We

A DECADE OF DISCOVERY

Since 2001 the Society has supported the research of Zahi Hawass, secretary general of Egypt's Supreme Council of Antiquities and a National Geographic explorer-in-residence. He is the author of *Zahi Hawass's Travel Guide to Secret Egypt*, forthcoming from National Geographic Books.

Kenneth Garrett has photographed 15 stories on Egypt for the magazine and collaborated with Zahi Hawass on six books.

set up two state-of-the-art DNA-sequencing labs, one in the basement of the Egyptian Museum in Cairo and the other at the Faculty of Medicine at Cairo University. The research would be led by Egyptian scientists: Yehia Gad and Somaia Ismail from the National Research Center in Cairo. We also decided to carry out CT scans of all the mummies, under the direction of Ashraf Selim and Sahar Saleem of the Faculty of Medicine at Cairo University. Three international experts served as consultants: Carsten Pusch of the Eberhard Karls University of Tübingen, Germany; Albert Zink of the EURAC-Institute for Mummies and the Iceman in Bolzano, Italy; and Paul Gostner of the Central Hospital Bolzano.

The identities of four of the mummies were known. These included Tutankhamun himself, still in his tomb in the Valley of the Kings, and three mummies on display at the Egyptian Museum: Amenhotep III, and Yuya and Tuyu, the parents of Amenhotep III's great queen, Tiye. Among the unidentified mummies was a male found in a mysterious tomb in the Valley of the Kings known as KV55. Archaeological and textual evidence suggested this mummy was most likely Akhenaten or Smenkhkare.

Our search for Tutankhamun's mother and wife focused on four unidentified females. Two of these, nicknamed the "Elder Lady" and the "Younger Lady," had been discovered in 1898, unwrapped and casually laid on the floor of a side chamber in the tomb of Amenhotep II (KV35), evidently hidden there by priests after the end of the New Kingdom, around 1000 B.C. The other two anonymous females were from a small tomb (KV21) in the Valley of the Kings. The architecture of this tomb suggests a date in the 18th dynasty, and both mummies hold their left fist against their chest in what is generally interpreted as a queenly pose.

Finally, we would attempt to obtain DNA from the fetuses in Tutankhamun's tomb—not a promising prospect given the extremely poor condition of these mummies. But if we succeeded, we might be able to fill in the missing pieces to a royal puzzle extending over five generations.

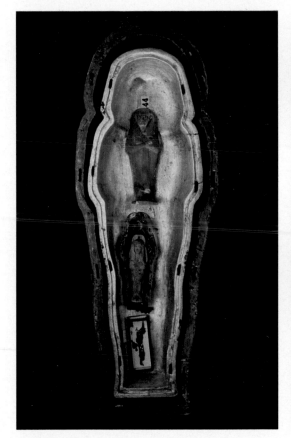

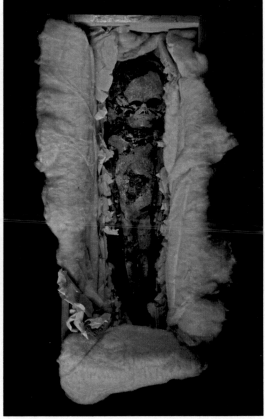

The innermost coffin of a miniature nested set from Tut's tomb was inscribed with the name of Tiye. Inside lay a lock of hair (above, box at bottom), perhaps a memento of a beloved grandmother.

A mummified fetus of at least seven months' gestation (above right) was found in Tut's tomb along with a tinier, more fragile fetus. One or both may have been the pharaoh's daughters.

TO OBTAIN WORKABLE samples, the geneticists extracted tissue from several different locations in each mummy, always from deep within the bone, where there was no chance the specimen would be contaminated by the DNA of previous archaeologists—or of the Egyptian priests who had performed the mummification. Extreme care was also taken to avoid any contamination by the researchers themselves. After the samples were extracted, the DNA had to be separated from unwanted substances, including the unguents and resins the priests had used to preserve the bodies. Since the embalming material varied with each mummy, so did the steps needed to purify the DNA. In each case the fragile material could be destroyed at every step.

At the center of the study was Tutankhamun himself. If the extraction and isolation

FATHER

Akhenaten ᴋᴠ55

The identity of King Tut's father has long been
a mystery. One candidate is the heretic pharaoh,
Akhenaten, who abandoned the gods of the state to
worship a single deity. In 1907 a badly decayed
mummy was discovered in KV55, a small tomb in the
Valley of the Kings containing a jumble of artifacts
connected to various kings and queens of the late 18th
dynasty. Royal epithets on the defaced coffin
suggested the body inside might be Akhenaten. DNA
now confirms the mummy to be a son of Amenhotep III
and Queen Tiye—known to be the parents of
Akhenaten—and the father of King Tut.

ROYAL RELATIONS

Genetic testing on 11 mummies revealed the remains of Tut's parents, who were brother and sister. Tut's father is very likely Akhenaten. The identity of his mother is still unknown.

HOW DO WE KNOW? Scientists collected DNA, then looked at eight sets of genetic markers (colored boxes in diagram below) to create a genetic fingerprint. Numerals in squares indicate the number of times a pattern of DNA is repeated. Shared numbers help determine kinship.

DNA ORIGIN
- ◻ Yuya
- ◻ Tuyu
- ◻ Amenhotep III
- ◻ Non-transmitted DNA
- ◻ Insufficient data

- ═══ Brother and sister
- ─ ─ Proposed relationship, insufficient data
- ♂ Male
- ♀ Female
- ⚑ Pharaoh

GREAT-GRANDPARENTS

♂ **Yuya** (KV46)
`11 13 | 6 15 | 22 27 | 29 34 | 6 10 | 12 22 | 9 12 | 20 25`

TOMB WHERE FOUND

♀ **Tuyu** (KV46)
`9 12 | 10 13 | 19 26 | 26 35 | 11 13 | 8 19 | 7 12 | 24 28`

GRANDPARENTS

Paired genetic markers: one inherited from each parent

⚑ ♂ **Amenhotep III** (KV35)
`10 16 | 6 15 | 16 27 | 25 34 | 8 13 | 16 22 | 6 9 | 23 31`

♀ **Tiye** (KV35EL)
`11 12 | 10 15 | 22 26 | 26 29 | 6 11 | 19 22 | 9 12 | 20 26`

PARENTS

Marker 12 passed from Tuyu to Tiye, then from Tiye to a son and daughter. One of them passed the marker to their son Tutankhamun.

⚑ ♂ **Akhenaten** (KV55)
`10 12 | 15 15 | 16 26 | 29 34 | 11 13 | 16 19 | 9 12 | 20 23`

♀ **Name unknown** (KV35YL)
`10 12 | 6 10 | 16 26 | 25 29 | 8 11 | 16 19 | 6 12 | 20 23`

KING TUT

Wife of Tut
KV21A (possibly Ankhesenamun) is the more likely candidate for Tut's wife and the mother of the fetuses:

♀ **Name unknown** (KV21A)
`10 16 | ▢ ▢ | 26 | 35 8 | 10 | ▢ 12 | 23`

♀ **Name unknown** (KV21B)
`10 | ▢ | 17 26 | ▢ | 11 13 | ▢ 12 | ▢`

⚑ ♂ **Tutankhamun** (KV62)
`10 12 | 10 15 | 16 26 | 29 34 | 8 13 | 19 19 | 6 12 | 23 23`

CHILDREN

♀ **Fetus 1** (KV62)
`12 16 | 10 13 | 16 | ▢ 29 | 8 | ▢ 19 | 12 23`

♀ **Fetus 2** (KV62)
`10 | 6 15 | 26 29 35 | 8 13 | 10 19 | ▢ 12 23`

JUAN VELASCO, AMANDA HOBBS, AND LAWSON PARKER, NGM STAFF. SOURCES: ZAHI HAWASS, SUPREME COUNCIL OF ANTIQUITIES, EGYPT.

succeeded, his DNA would be captured in a clear liquid solution, ready to be analyzed. To our dismay, however, the initial solutions turned out a murky black. Six months of hard work were required to figure out how to remove the contaminant—some still unidentified product of the mummification process—and obtain a sample ready for amplifying and sequencing.

After we had obtained DNA as well from the three other male mummies in the sample—Yuya, Amenhotep III, and the mysterious KV55—we set out to clarify the identity of Tutankhamun's father. On this critical issue the archaeological record was ambiguous. In several inscriptions from his reign, Tutankhamun refers to Amenhotep III as his father, but this cannot be taken as conclusive, since the term used could also be interpreted to mean "grandfather" or "ancestor." Also, according to the generally accepted chronology, Amenhotep III died about a decade before Tutankhamun was born.

Many scholars believe that his father was instead Akhenaten. Supporting this view is a broken limestone block found near Amarna that bears inscriptions calling both Tutankhaten and Ankhesenpaaten beloved children of the king. Since we know that Ankhesenpaaten was the daughter of Akhenaten, it follows that Tutankhaten (later Tutankhamun) was his son. Not all scholars find this evidence convincing, however, and some have argued that Tutankhamun's father was in fact the mysterious Smenkhkare. I always favored Akhenaten myself, but it was only a theory.

Once the mummies' DNA was isolated, it was a fairly simple matter to compare the Y chromosomes of Amenhotep III, KV55, and Tutankhamun and see that they were indeed related. (Related males share the same pattern of DNA in their Y chromosome, since this part of a male's genome is inherited directly from his father.) But to clarify their precise relationship required a more refined kind of genetic fingerprinting. Along the chromosomes in our genomes there are specific known regions where the pattern of DNA letters—the A's, T's, G's, and C's that make up our genetic code—

varies greatly between one person and another. These variations amount to different numbers of repeated sequences of the same few letters. Where one person might have a sequence of letters repeated ten times, for instance, another unrelated person might have the same sequence stuttered 15 times, a third person 20, and so on. A match between ten of these highly variable regions is enough for the FBI to conclude that the DNA left at a crime scene and that of a suspect might be one and the same.

Reuniting the members of a family separated 3,300 years ago requires a little less stringency than the standards needed to solve a crime. By comparing just eight of these variable regions, our team was able to establish with a probability of better than 99.99 percent that Amenhotep III was the father of the individual in KV55, who was in turn the father of Tutankhamun.

We now knew we had the body of Tut's father—but we still did not know for certain who he was. Our chief suspects were Akhenaten and Smenkhkare. The KV55 tomb contained a cache of material thought to have been brought by Tutankhamun to Thebes from Amarna, where Akhenaten (and perhaps Smenkhkare) had been buried. Though the coffin's cartouches—oval rings containing the pharaoh's names—had been chiseled off, the coffin bore epithets associated only with Akhenaten himself. But not all the evidence pointed to Akhenaten. Most forensic analyses had concluded that the body inside was that of a man no older than 25—too young to be Akhenaten, who seems to have sired two daughters before beginning his 17-year reign. Most scholars thus suspected the mummy was instead the shadowy pharaoh Smenkhkare.

Now a new witness could be called on to help resolve this mystery. The so-called Elder Lady (KV35EL) mummy is lovely even in death, with long reddish hair falling across her shoulders. A strand of this hair had previously been matched morphologically to a lock of hair buried within a nest of miniature coffins in Tutankhamun's tomb, inscribed with the name of Queen Tiye, wife of Amenhotep III—and mother of Akhenaten. By comparing the DNA of the

Elder Lady with that from the mummies of Tiye's known parents, Yuya and Tuyu, we confirmed that the Elder Lady was indeed Tiye. Now she could testify whether the KV55 mummy was indeed her son.

Much to our delight, the comparison of their DNA proved the relationship. New CT scans of the KV55 mummy also revealed an

AKHENATEN HAD CONCEIVED A SON WITH HIS OWN SISTER. THE CHILD WOULD BE KNOWN AS TUTANKHAMUN.

age-related degeneration in the spine and osteoarthritis in the knees and legs. It appeared that he had died closer to the age of 40 than 25, as originally thought. With the age discrepancy thus resolved, we could conclude that the KV55 mummy, the son of Amenhotep III and Tiye and the father of Tutankhamun, is almost certainly Akhenaten. (Since we know so little about Smenkhkare, he cannot be completely ruled out.)

Our renewed CT scanning of the mummies also put to rest the notion that the family suffered from some congenital disease, such as Marfan syndrome, that might explain the elongated faces and feminized appearance seen in the art from the Amarna period. No such pathologies were found. Akhenaten's androgynous depiction in the art would seem instead to be a stylistic reflection of his identification with the god Aten, who was both male and female and thus the source of all life.

And what of Tutankhamun's mother? To our surprise, the DNA of the so-called Younger Lady (KV35YL), found lying beside Tiye in the alcove of KV35, matched that of the boy king. More amazing still, her DNA proved that, like Akhenaten, she was the daughter of Amenhotep III and Tiye. Akhenaten had conceived a son with his own sister. Their child would be known as Tutankhamun.

With this discovery, we now know that it is unlikely that either of Akhenaten's known wives, Nefertiti and a second wife named Kiya, was Tutankhamun's mother, since there is no evidence from the historical record that either was his full sister. We know the names of five daughters of Amenhotep III and Tiye, but we will probably never know which of Akhenaten's sisters bore him a child. But to me, knowing her name is less important than the relationship with her brother. Incest was not uncommon among ancient Egyptian royalty. But I believe that in this case, it planted the seed of their son's early death.

THE RESULTS of our DNA analysis, published in February in the *Journal of the American Medical Association,* convinced me that genetics can provide a powerful new tool for enhancing our understanding of Egyptian history, especially when combined with radiological studies of the mummies and insights gleaned from the archaeological record.

Nowhere is this more evident than in our quest to understand the cause of Tutankhamun's death. When we began the new study, Ashraf Selim and his colleagues discovered something previously unnoticed in the CT images of the mummy: Tutankhamun's left foot was clubbed, one toe was missing a bone, and the bones in part of the foot were destroyed by necrosis—literally, "tissue death." Both the clubbed foot and the bone disease would have impeded his ability to walk. Scholars had already noted that 130 partial or whole walking sticks had been found in Tutankhamun's tomb, some of which show clear signs of use.

Some have argued that such staffs were common symbols of power and that the damage to Tutankhamun's foot may have occurred during the mummification process. But our analysis showed that new bone growth had occurred in response to the necrosis, proving the condition was present during his lifetime. And of all the pharaohs, only Tutankhamun is shown seated while performing activities such as shooting an arrow from a bow or using a throw stick. This was not a king who held a staff just as a symbol of power. This was a young man who needed a cane to walk.

Tutankhamun's bone disease was crippling, but on its own would not have been fatal. To look further into possible causes of his death, we tested his mummy for genetic traces of various infectious diseases. I was skeptical that the geneticists would be able to find such evidence—and I was delighted to be proved wrong. Based on the presence of DNA from several strains of a parasite called *Plasmodium falciparum,* it was evident that Tutankhamun was infected with malaria—indeed, he had contracted the most severe form of the disease multiple times.

Did malaria kill the king? Perhaps. The disease can trigger a fatal immune response in the body, cause circulatory shock, and lead to hemorrhaging, convulsions, coma, and death. As other scientists have pointed out, however, malaria was probably common in the region at the time, and Tutankhamun may have acquired partial immunity to the disease. On the other hand, it may well have weakened his immune system, leaving him more vulnerable to complications that might have followed the unhealed fracture of his leg we evaluated in 2005.

In my view, however, Tutankhamun's health was compromised from the moment he was conceived. His mother and father were full brother and sister. Pharaonic Egypt was not the only society in history to institutionalize royal incest, which can have political advantages. (See "The Risks and Rewards of Royal Incest," page 60.) But there can be a dangerous consequence. Married siblings are more likely to pass on twin copies of harmful genes, leaving their children vulnerable to a variety of genetic defects. Tutankhamun's malformed foot may have been one such flaw. We suspect he also had a partially cleft palate, another congenital defect. Perhaps he struggled against others until a severe bout of malaria or a leg broken in an accident added one strain too many to a body that could no longer carry the load.

There may be one other poignant testimony to the legacy of royal incest buried with Tutankhamun in his tomb. While the data are still incomplete, our study suggests that one of the mummified fetuses found there is the daughter of Tutankhamun himself, and the other fetus is probably his child as well. So far we have been able to obtain only partial data for the two female mummies from KV21. One of them, KV21A, may well be the infants' mother and thus, Tutankhamun's wife, Ankhesenamun. We know from history that she was the daughter of Akhenaten and Nefertiti, and thus likely her husband's half sister. Another consequence of inbreeding can be children whose genetic defects do not allow them to be brought to term.

So perhaps this is where the play ends, at least for now: with a young king and his queen trying, but failing, to conceive a living heir for the throne of Egypt. Among the many splendid artifacts buried with Tutankhamun is a small ivory-paneled box, carved with a scene of the royal couple. Tutankhamun is leaning on his cane while his wife holds out to him a bunch of flowers. In this and other depictions, they appear serenely in love. The failure of that love to bear fruit ended not just a family but also a dynasty. We know that after Tutankhamun's death, an Egyptian queen, most likely Ankhesenamun, appeals to the king of the Hittites, Egypt's principal enemies, to send a prince to marry her, because "my husband is dead, and I have no son." The Hittite king sends one of his sons, but he dies before reaching Egypt. I believe he was murdered by Horemheb, the commander in chief of Tutankhamun's armies, who eventually takes the throne for himself. But Horemheb too dies childless, leaving the throne to a fellow army commander.

The new pharaoh's name was Ramses I. With him begins another dynasty, one which, under the rule of his grandson Ramses the Great, would see Egypt rise to new heights of imperial power. More than anyone else, this great king would work to erase from history all traces of Akhenaten, Tutankhamun, and the other "heretics" of the Amarna period. With our investigations, we seek to honor them and keep their memories alive. ☐

TUT

Tutankhamun KV62

Offspring of a union between siblings, this often studied pharaoh is now revealed to have had a congenital clubfoot afflicted with bone disease, which would have made walking painful. Inbreeding may have caused the deformity and even prevented him from producing an heir with his wife, who was probably his half sister. Whatever flaws King Tut inherited in this life, however, the image he left for eternity is one of luminous perfection—his iconic funeral mask crafted of gold, regarded by the ancient Egyptians as the flesh of the gods.

WIFE

KV21A

When tomb KV21 was found in 1817, two well-
preserved female mummies lay inside. Vandals later
ripped them apart. Preliminary DNA results suggest that
the one now missing her head (below) could be the
mother of at least one of the fetuses from King Tut's tomb.
If so, she is most likely Ankhesenamun, a daughter of
Akhenaten and the only known wife of Tutankhamun.
An ivory-paneled box (right), also from Tut's tomb, shows
him with his beloved queen. New information
about his health suggests that he probably needed
to use the staff he holds as a crutch.

THE RISKS AND REWARDS OF ROYAL INCEST

King Tut's family was not the only royalty to have close relations among its close relations.

WHEN NEW ENGLAND MISSIONARY Hiram Bingham arrived in Hawaii in 1820, he was dismayed to find the natives indulging in idolatry, hula dancing, and, among the ruling family, incest. The Hawaiians themselves did not share Bingham's shock at the royals' behavior. Royal incest, notes historian Joanne Carando, was "not only accepted but even encouraged" in Hawaii as an exclusive royal privilege.

In fact, while virtually every culture in recorded history has held sibling or parent-child couplings taboo, royalty have been exempted in many societies, including ancient Egypt, Inca Peru, and, at times, Central Africa, Mexico, and Thailand. And while royal families in Europe avoided sibling incest, many, including the Hohenzollerns of Prussia, the Bourbons of France, and the British royal family, often married cousins. The Spanish Habsburgs, who ruled for nearly 200 years, frequently married among close relatives. Their dynasty ended in 1700 with the death of Charles II, a king so riddled with

When Western values pressed ashore, Hawaii's King Kamehameha III (above) donned a suit, but skirted a ban on royal incest. Thailand's King Rama V, posing with his half sister—and wife—and their children, faced no such prohibition.

health and development problems that he didn't talk until he was four or walk until he was eight. He also had trouble chewing food and couldn't sire a child.

The physical problems faced by Charles and the pharaoh Tutankhamun, the son of siblings, point to one possible explanation for the near-universal incest taboo: Overlapping genes can backfire. Siblings share half their genes on average, as do parents and offspring. First cousins' genomes overlap 12.5 percent. Matings between close relatives can raise the danger that harmful recessive genes, especially if combined repeatedly through generations, will match up in the offspring, leading to elevated chances of health or developmental problems—perhaps Tut's partially cleft palate and congenitally deformed foot or Charles's small stature and impotence.

If the royals knew of these potential downsides, they chose to ignore them. According to Stanford University classics professor Walter Scheidel, one reason is that "incest sets them

apart." Royal incest occurs mainly in societies where rulers have tremendous power and no peers, except the gods. Since gods marry each other, so should royals.

Incest also protects royal assets. Marrying family members ensures that a king will share riches, privilege, and power only with people already his relatives. In dominant, centralized societies such as ancient Egypt or Inca Peru, this can mean limiting the mating circle to immediate family. In societies with overlapping cultures, as in second-millennium Europe, it can mean marrying extended family members from other regimes to forge alliances while keeping power among kin.

And the hazards, while real, are not absolute. Even the high rates of genetic overlap generated in the offspring of sibling unions, for instance, can create more healthy children than sick ones. And royal wealth can help offset some medical conditions; Charles II lived far better (and probably longer, dying at age 38) than he would have were he a peasant.

A king or a pharaoh can also hedge the risk of his incestuous bets by placing wagers elsewhere. He can mate, as Stanford classicist Josiah Ober notes, "with pretty much anybody he wants to." Inca ruler Huayna Capac (1493-1527), for instance, passed power not only to his son Huáscar, whose mother was Capac's wife and sister, but also to his son Atahualpa, whose mother was apparently a consort. And King Rama V of Thailand (1873-1910) sired more than 70 children—some from marriages to half sisters but most with dozens of consorts and concubines. Such a ruler could opt to funnel wealth, security, education, and even political power to many of his children, regardless of the status of the mother. A geneticist would say he was offering his genes many paths to the future.

It can all seem rather mercenary. Yet affection sometimes drives these bonds. Bingham learned that even after King Kamehameha III of Hawaii accepted Christian rule, he slept for several years with his sister, Princess Nahiʻenaʻena—pleasing their elders but disturbing the missionaries. They did it, says historian Carando, because they loved each other. —*David Dobbs*

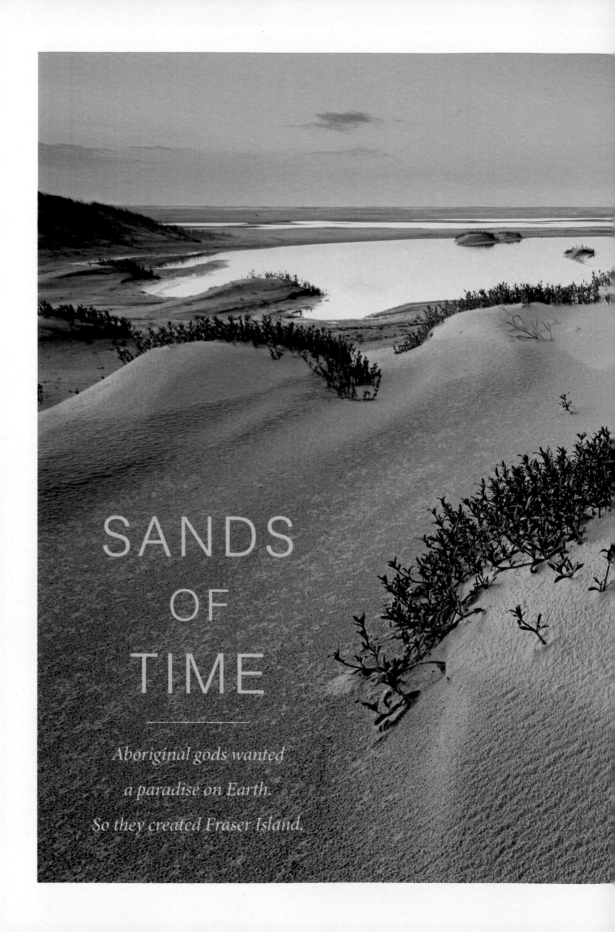

SANDS
OF
TIME

*Aboriginal gods wanted
a paradise on Earth.
So they created Fraser Island.*

Pioneering plants get a toehold above the tide line on Australia's Fraser Island.

Following its keen nose, a dingo prowls the edge of a sand blow—an ever shifting expanse of silica.

Tannin-rich runoff from Fraser's interior stains the sea in the aftermath of a summer storm.

By Roff Smith

Photographs by Peter Essick

Iron oxide colors Arch Cliff a luminous red, one of a palette of hues seen in Fraser's mineral-rich sands. Bound together by a kind of natural cement, some dunes rise 800 feet high. Trees and other vegetation manage to survive thanks to fungi that release nutrients from the sand.

I t wasn't enough simply to create the world; the Aboriginal god Beeral wanted it to be beautiful as well. And so he sent two trusted messengers, Yindingie and his spirit helper K'gari, to render the raw material of creation into a paradise. They did such a splendid job that by the time they were finished, K'gari longed to stay in this wonderful place forever. She lay down in the warm waters of a particularly beautiful bay, and there she went to sleep.

While she slept, Yindingie transformed her body into a long, slender island of crystalline sand, the largest such island in all the world. He clothed her with the most luxuriant of rain forests, painted her soft, sandy skin a rainbow of colors, and fashioned a chain of jewel-like lakes to be her eyes into heaven. He filled the air with colorful birds, and then, so she would never be lonely, he set a tribe of Aborigines on the island—the Butchulla people, who passed down the story of its creation and in whose language K'gari came to be the word for "paradise."

A lot of water has washed its shores since then. Today paradise goes by the name of Fraser Island, renamed by newcomers after a Scottish sea captain and his wife were famously marooned here among the Aborigines in 1836. But by any name or reckoning, it remains a place apart, with an uncanny ability to weave itself into the dreams of all who draw near.

Fraser Island's storied landscapes have inspired many of Australia's greatest writers and artists, and its delicate ecosystems fired passions in one of Australia's first great grassroots

---

Roff Smith has covered every corner of Australia, his adopted country since 1981. Peter Essick specializes in nature and environmental photography.

environmental campaigns in the 1970s, stopping the mining of its mineral-rich sands and bringing an eventual end to logging on the island. And for succeeding generations of locals and visitors alike, it has been a prism through which to see and appreciate the often nuanced beauty of the Australian bush.

For all the paintings, poetry, and prose Fraser Island has inspired, this is not an easy place to categorize. One moment you're hiking through a cathedral rain forest, all giant ferns and piccabeen palms, and the next you're in fragrant eucalyptus woodland, gazing through a break in the trees at a sea of golden dunes—and beyond them, in the soft, summery haze, rolling coastal heaths bright with wildflowers. Changes in landscape that logic tells you should be hundreds of miles apart happen here one after the

other, as swiftly and magically as a twist of a kaleidoscope barrel.

The greatest wonder of all, perhaps, is that most everything here grows on nothing more substantial than sand held in place by humble fungi. No dreamscape could be woven of slenderer thread.

"I like to think of this island as a living organism in its own right, like the Great Barrier Reef," says Peter Meyer, a naturalist who has been living and working as a guide on Fraser Island for the past 15 years. "But here, instead of coral polyps, it's mycorrhizal fungi and their symbiotic relationship with plants that's the basis for everything. By liberating the nutrients in the sand, they make it possible for all these amazing things to grow. Without the fungi, this would be just another sandbar."

Make that a very big sandbar: more than 75 miles long, about 15 miles wide, and with dunes soaring to 800 feet. Sand has been accumulating along this stretch of the Queensland coast for some 750,000 years, in part because volcanic bedrock here provides a natural catchment for sediment moved up the eastern seaboard by a powerful longshore current.

English navigator James Cook, who sailed along this coast in 1770, was the first European known to have sighted Fraser Island. The globe-trotting Yorkshireman didn't think much of it, dismissing it with a few cursory lines in his journal. Likewise explorer Matthew Flinders, who landed here some 30 years later. Wilderness in those days was a commodity to be tamed and brought to profitable service, not admired for its own sake.

From that perspective, the interior of the island pleased Edward Armitage, an early 20th-century timber merchant. It is from his pen that we have some of the first descriptions of Fraser's magnificent rain forests, as he lamented that many of "these great Monarchs of the forest" were too big for the sawmills of the day.

The future soon supplied bigger machinery, and for more than a century the forests here were heavily logged. The dense timber was

The world's largest sand island, Fraser was formed over some 750,000 years by current and wind, which transport tons of sand up Australia's east coast (map). The island is named for Captain James Fraser, who, with his wife Eliza, was shipwrecked there in 1836. Eliza's sensational—and often contradictory—accounts of the ordeal include lurid tales of the murder and torture of passengers by local "savages," depicted in this illustration from an 1838 book.

shipped around the world and used for such empire-building projects as lining the Suez Canal and, after World War II, for rebuilding London's Tilbury Docks.

A rare early tourist appeared on the scene in the late 1940s. Sidney Nolan, one of Australia's greatest 20th-century painters, had been traveling through Queensland, looking for inspiration in the landscape. He found it in the nearly forgotten story of shipwreck and survival that a century earlier had given Fraser Island its name.

In 1836 the *Stirling Castle,* commanded by Captain James Fraser, set sail from Sydney to Singapore with 18 crew and passengers, whose

number included the captain's wife, Eliza. Some days later, as the ship threaded its way through the labyrinthine passages of the Great Barrier Reef, it holed itself on the coral and began slowly sinking. Passengers and crew bundled themselves into two lifeboats and set off down the coast toward a settlement at Moreton Bay (now Brisbane), hundreds of miles to the south. It was a harrowing journey, not least for Eliza, who reportedly was heavily pregnant at the time and wound up giving birth in the badly leaking longboat; the infant died shortly afterward.

Things grew worse for the embattled survivors in the longboat *(Continued on page 78)*

Ridges of peat and pools of dark, acidic water form a patterned peatland near Moon Point.

Wind and rain lash the face of Red Canyon, an ancient dune complex on the island's eastern flank.

Coffee-colored Wathumba Creek spills into the jade shallows of Platypus Bay.

carrying Captain and Mrs. Fraser. As their flimsy craft grew more and more unseaworthy, the other boat abandoned them and sailed on. Finally, more than a month after the shipwreck, they were forced to beach themselves on what was then known as the Great Sandy Island.

What happened next is unclear. Some accounts say the survivors bartered with the Butchulla people, giving up their clothing in exchange for food. Others claim the Aborigines stripped the castaways naked and treated them as slaves. Either way, it seems likely that hunger, disease, and exhaustion finished off most of the survivors, including Captain Fraser.

For her part, Eliza later claimed that she had been forced to work as a drudge around the Aborigines' camp, gathering firewood and digging up roots. Word of her plight eventually reached

One of dozens of lakes on the island, Lake McKenzie shimmers in the starlight. During the day the lake's sugar white beach and windowpane water attract hundreds of visitors. Like the painters and poets who celebrated Fraser's otherworldly allure, they return home with stories and images of soul-stirring beauty.

the authorities at Moreton Bay. A rescue party was sent out, and an Irish convict named John Graham, who had previously lived in the bush as an escapee and who spoke the Aboriginal language, ultimately negotiated her release.

The rest of the story follows in the finest tabloid tradition. Within months of her rescue, Eliza met and married another sea captain, moved to England, and went on to become a sideshow attraction in London's Hyde Park. There she spun increasingly wild tales of murder, torture, white slavery, and cannibalism to spellbound audiences at sixpence a head.

Alas for Eliza, nothing fades quicker than yesterday's news, and she soon lapsed into obscurity. She is said to have moved to New Zealand and was killed in a carriage accident during a visit to Melbourne in 1858.

Sidney Nolan was captivated by the operatic quality of Eliza Fraser's tale and the rich symbolism of Europeans, stripped of their civilizing veneer, grubbing for survival in an alien landscape. So the artist hopped on a timber barge and went to see Fraser Island for himself.

"The psyche of the place has bitten into me deeply," he wrote to a friend. Its spell would remain on him for the rest of his life, inspiring two series of paintings and dozens of canvases. Nolan in turn passed on his fascination to his friend Patrick White, a Nobel Prize-winning author who visited the island in the 1960s and early 1970s. White used its primal wilderness as the setting for his 1973 novel *The Eye of the Storm* and again in *A Fringe of Leaves,* a fictionalized retelling of Eliza's saga.

In 1770 Captain Cook had been unimpressed by the scrubby, sandy bluffs visible from his ship. Little more than 200 years later artists and writers, scientists and statesmen saw such value in Fraser Island that in 1992 it was declared a World Heritage site. Having helped transform Australians' sense of wild beauty, the island now draws boatloads of admirers—an outcome wise old Beeral might have hoped for when he sent Yindingie and K'gari to beautify the world those many eons ago. □

The island's geographic
isolation created a wonderland
of biological richness. Now
population pressures and political
turmoil speed the plunder of its
rosewood, minerals, and gems.

THE
PIERCED
HEART

OF MADAGASCAR

AVENUE OF THE BAOBABS, an area near Morondava
protected since 2007, is all that remains of a once
thick forest cleared for farmland. Growing 80 feet
or more, baobabs are valued for fruit and bark.

THEIR EFFORTS scored in the earth like tree rings, laborers dig for sapphires near Ilakaka, a boomtown since the gems were discovered there in 1998. The area once supplied a third of the world's sapphires, but today exports have dropped sharply.

A LOCAL MARKET in the highland city of Antsirabe draws flower sellers as well as hungry children begging for handouts. Fewer families send their kids to school as the economy reels from falloffs in aid and tourism following a 2009 coup.

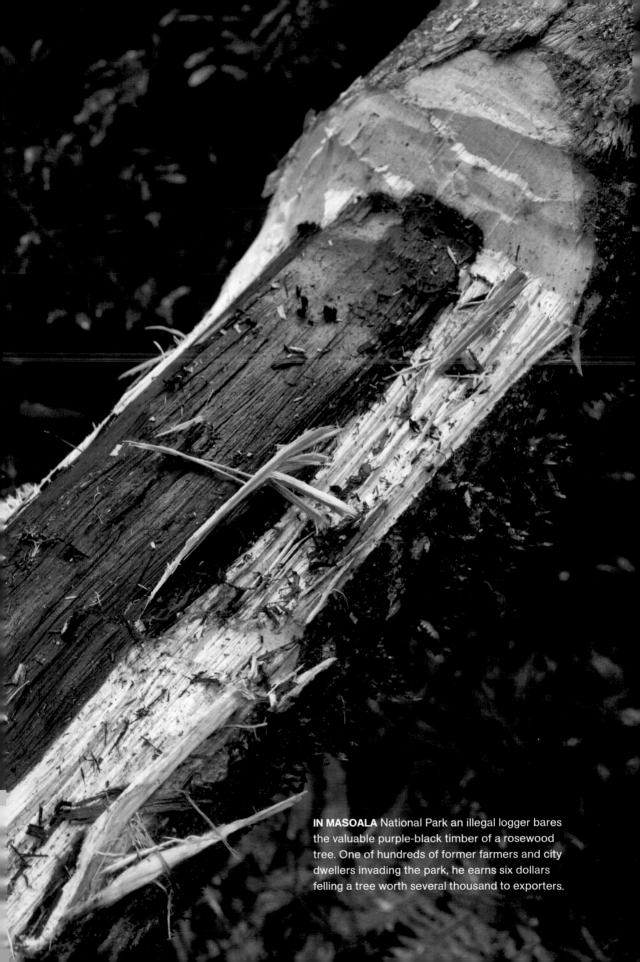

IN MASOALA National Park an illegal logger bares the valuable purple-black timber of a rosewood tree. One of hundreds of former farmers and city dwellers invading the park, he earns six dollars felling a tree worth several thousand to exporters.

FAR FROM ANY law enforcement, a camp swells with workers and rosewood logs on the Ankavia River. Alarmed conservationists report that loggers ax as many as 200 trees a day in national parks, despite the ban on rosewood exports.

BY ROBERT DRAPER

PHOTOGRAPHS BY PASCAL MAITRE

THE YOUNG MAN in the shorts and sleeveless T-shirt stands in his pirogue and pulls it upstream with a long bamboo pole. The Onive River is shallow and moves swiftly against him. Overhead a brooding sky opens up and dispenses barrages of rain, then sunlight, then more rain. The young man, whose name is Remon, is as heedless of the weather as the crocodiles lying prostrate on the shore.

Gliding past him in the opposite direction, one every three minutes, are other piroguemen. Remon calls out to them; they holler back. They are his river mates, each ferrying a dark, monstrous log of illegally harvested rosewood downstream from the rain forest to the lumberyards in the northeastern Madagascan city of Antalaha. There a paycheck awaits. Once Remon drops us off at the edge of the forest, he will do the same.

Remon doesn't like the work. The timber boss who employs him—but whose name he does not know—has told Remon that he must paddle all day without pause because the rangers have been bribed to stay away for only a finite period, after which another bribe will be expected. Still, transporting the fallen trees is better than cutting them down, which had been Remon's previous job. He quit after concluding that the risks had become too great. While illegal logging had been going on for years, the pace had suddenly escalated: The forest was unpoliced and filled with organized gangs, a free-for-all of deforestation spurred by the collapse of Madagascar's government in March of 2009 and by the insatiable appetite of Chinese timber procurers, who imported more than 200 million dollars' worth of rosewood from the country's northeastern forests in just a few months. One rosewood cutter Remon knew had been robbed of his harvest by forest thugs who told him, "There's 30 of us, one of you." And he's just heard that two men were decapitated with a machete over a timber dispute a few days ago.

The river grows still, and Remon lights a cigarette of tobacco and marijuana. He speaks of the *fady,* the taboos that protected the forest for centuries. There is always anxious talk among the timber thieves whenever an errant tree crushes a skull or the river rapids shatter a leg: *We have angered our ancestors. They are punishing us.* Elders have lectured Remon about pillaging sacred turf.

"Fine," he tells them. "Try feeding the trees to your family."

REMON USED TO FEED his family by working in the vanilla fields outside of Antalaha, a coastal town that is, like the island itself, rich in resources and poor in every other way. Two decades ago Madagascar's president at the time, Didier Ratsiraka, was so proud of Antalaha's reputation as the world's vanilla capital that he dispatched an official to pay tribute to the town. "He thought we would be full of big buildings and paved roads," says a longtime vanilla exporter, Michel Lomone. "The president was very disappointed by the report his counselor gave him."

Since then a succession of cyclones and slumping prices have conspired to jostle the crown

RISKING LIFE AND CARGO, a deliveryman rides Onive River rapids. His 400-pound rosewood log is tied to a raft of lighter wood to keep it afloat. On slower water (below) a crew ferries a truck loaded with logs. Most end up in China to make high-cost furniture and musical instruments.

from the vanilla king's head. Today Antalaha is dusty and somnolent, and though its main boulevard, Rue de Tananarive, was finally paved in 2005 with funding from the European Union, the street's traffic consists largely of a few dinky taxis, rusty bicycles, chickens, goats, and, above all, pedestrians striding barefoot in the rain and holding over their heads the elephantine leaves known as traveler's palms to stay dry.

Or such was the traffic until the spring of 2009. During that season the streets of Antalaha suddenly began to roar with motorcycles. The one store on Rue de Tananarive that carried such vehicles promptly sold out. Responding to the demand, a second store opened up down the street and began doing crazy business as well. The buyers were rawboned young men, and everyone in Antalaha knew where their fleeting cash came from. It wasn't the vanilla fields. The same young men could be seen driving into town in the backs of pickup trucks astraddle great loads of illegally harvested timber, systematically filling their pockets by selectively cutting Madagascar's precious rosewood trees from the forest.

Madagascar is an island—the world's fourth largest, at over 225,000 square miles, but an island nonetheless. Though all islands are blessed with their own unique biosphere, Madagascar (which was dislocated from Africa some 165 million years ago) is a special case: Roughly 90 percent of its flora and fauna is found nowhere else on the planet. The extraterrestrial spectacle of carrot-shaped baobab trees, ghostly lemurs, and whole "forests" of towering stone spikes is inclined to make the world-weariest of visitors grow wide-eyed with innocent delight.

Its rare and haunting beauty coexists with a desperation among its people that defines everyday life. The Malagasy, the island's major ethnic group, have an expression that is elegant in its fatalism: *"Aleo maty rahampitso toy izay maty*

Writer Robert Draper and photographer Pascal Maitre reported on the failed state of Somalia for the September 2009 issue. The article won the National Magazine Award for photojournalism.

androany," or "It's better to die tomorrow rather than today." The typical Madagascan lives on about a dollar a day.

And considering that Madagascar's population of more than 20 million is growing 3 percent a year—one of the most rapid rates in Africa—the tension between rich land and poor residents on a finite landscape increases by the day. For this reason alarmed ecologists have termed Madagascar a biodiversity hot spot, deploring, in particular, the Malagasy practice of slash-and-burn agriculture, in which swaths of forest are torched and converted to rice fields. Just as the global environmental community rejoiced in 2002 when Marc Ravalomanana assumed the presidency on a green-friendly platform, so did they react with dismay in the spring of 2009 as the military routed Ravalomanana from office and installed a constitutionally underage former radio disc jockey in his place. As one veteran aid worker stationed in Madagascar said, "I feel like the past 25 years of work has been undone."

In September 2009, after months during which up to 460,000 dollars' worth of rosewood was being illegally harvested every day, the cash-strapped new government reversed a 2000 ban on the export of rosewood and released a decree legalizing the sale of stockpiled logs. Pressured by an alarmed international community, the government reinstated the ban in April. Yet logging continues.

The outside world is in no position to lecture, given its own voracious appetite—sometimes benign, sometimes less so—for Madagascar's wondrous resources. The raiding of the forests illustrates how easily the frail balance between human and ecological imperatives can be undone. But that balance has always been wobbly in Madagascar. Various foreign-owned holding groups own most of the rights to prospect and mine the country of its gold, nickel, cobalt, ilmenite, and sapphire (which once supplied a third of the world market). ExxonMobil began deep offshore oil exploration in Madagascar four years ago. Some of the finest American guitar makers have long featured fingerboards constructed of rare Madagascan ebony. In recent years the

A HIGH POPULATION GROWTH RATE MEANS THE TENSION BETWEEN RICH LAND AND POOR RESIDENTS INCREASES BY THE DAY.

island's federal government has attempted to lease arable land to the South Koreans and sell water to the Saudis. In this come-and-get-it climate, much is extracted but little is gained on behalf of the average Malagasy. Small wonder, then, that local miners loot the countryside of precious gemstones to be sold in Asian markets. Or that animals such as the leaf-tailed gecko and the endangered plowshare tortoise are smuggled by small operators off the island to collectors. Or that the rawboned young men of Antalaha would decide it's better to die tomorrow while taking the money of Chinese rosewood buyers today.

"It's good for the economy, bad for the ecology," observes one man involved in the illicit rosewood business, smiling and shrugging as he hops on his motorcycle and speeds off. But the boomlet in Antalaha has proved to be a false one. Even leaving aside the devastating, long-term consequences of a plundered forest—the disappearance of precious wood in as much as 25,000 acres of the country's 11.3 million acres of protected areas, the extinction of lemurs and other endemic species, a plague of soil erosion that silts up rivers and wipes out nearby farmland, the loss of tourism revenue—the perverse side effects of the rosewood raiding are more immediately felt. The residents of Antalaha who suddenly found themselves dodging motorcycle traffic also began to notice the price of fish, rice, and other daily goods begin to climb. The reason was simple: Fewer men were out at sea or in the fields.

"They're in the forest," says Michel Lomone, the vanilla exporter. "Everyone's gone to the forest."

TO GO FROM ANTALAHA to the forest—meaning Masoala National Park, Madagascar's largest—requires a journey no one would undertake who does not need to do so. It begins with a three-hour drive southwest from the town, along dirt roads so badly mangled from the weight of lumber trucks that vehicles sink into the muddy ditches, and locals must be rounded up to help push them out. Then comes the four-hour pirogue trip up the Onive River, followed by a four-hour slog on foot through spongy rice fields, and another two hours along a slippery mud trail up and down the granite spine of dense primary forest—all of this under sporadic rainfall. Thus does one arrive at the edge of Masoala. But to find rosewood that has not yet been cut, one must push deeper, for many hours.

The park's southwestern border is Antongil Bay, where humpback whales noisily give birth between July and September. Within the wild, green womb of the 580,000-acre tropical rain forest, a stranger's doggedness may be rewarded with cameo appearances by orchids, carnivorous plants, serpent eagles, the dazzling Parson's chameleon, and the red ruffed lemur. Masoala offers a seeming infinity of medicinal herbs, wild berries, and firewood to villagers, who stride barefoot in and out of the forest daily, singing and chatting. In contrast, the young men who are here from the city on business appear lost in this damp, mysterious thicket.

For weeks they camp out in small groups beside the trees they've singled out for cutting, subsisting on rice and coffee, until the boss shows up. He inspects the rosewood, gives the order. They chop away with axes. Within hours a tree that first took root perhaps 500 years ago has fallen to the ground. The cutters hack away at its white exterior until all that remains is its telltale violet heart. The rosewood is cut into logs about seven feet long. Another team of two men tie ropes around each log and proceed to drag it out of the forest to the river's edge, a feat that will take them two days and earn them $10 to $20 a log, depending on the distance. While staggering through the forest myself, from time to time I come upon the jarring apparition of two

RARE MADAGASCAR

Remnants of the island's original vegetation serve as critical biodiversity hot spots, crammed with hundreds of vulnerable endemic plant and animal species. Yet today only half of the high-priority sites lie within the country's network of protected areas. With the overthrow of the government, ambitious conservation plans are on hold, and illegal logging and poaching run rampant in parks.

DWINDLING WONDERS

Some 90 percent of Madagascar's plant and animal species are found nowhere else, having evolved in isolation for millions of years after the island broke from Africa and India. Many are restricted to small, unprotected biodiversity areas.

Plants

Most of Madagascar's estimated 13,000 plant species are endemic, like the threatened Grandidier's baobab, one of six baobab species unique to the island.

Mammals

Lemurs live only on Madagascar and the nearby Comoros islands. Fifty species make up nearly half of Madagascar's mammals. More than 20, including the silky sifaka, are endangered.

Antsirañana

Iharaña (Vohemar)

Sambava

Antalaha

Onive River

MASOALA NATIONAL PARK

MAROJEJY NATIONAL PARK

Ankavia R.

Maromokotro 9,436 ft 2,876 m

Maroantsetra

Antongil Bay

Current focus of illegal logging

Mahajanga

MADAGASCAR

AFRICA

Reptiles

Chameleons, such as the colorful lesser chameleon, likely originated on Madagascar; two-thirds of the species are found here. Reptiles are under pressure from the pet trade.

③

Birds

As many as three-quarters of the 108 endemic species live only in wooded areas, including the long-tailed ground roller, restricted to the spiny forest of the southwest.

④

Amphibians

This population is all frogs, with 99 percent of the 373 species endemic, including the critically endangered harlequin mantella, found only on the central high plateau.

⑤

WILLIAM E. MCNULTY, SAM PEPPLE, AND LISA R. RITTER, NGM STAFF; INTERNATIONAL MAPPING

ART: ALDO CHIAPPE

SOURCES: REBIOMA; MADAGASCAR PROTECTED AREAS SYSTEM; WILDLIFE CONSERVATION SOCIETY; ROYAL BOTANIC GARDENS, KEW; MISSOURI BOTANICAL GARDEN

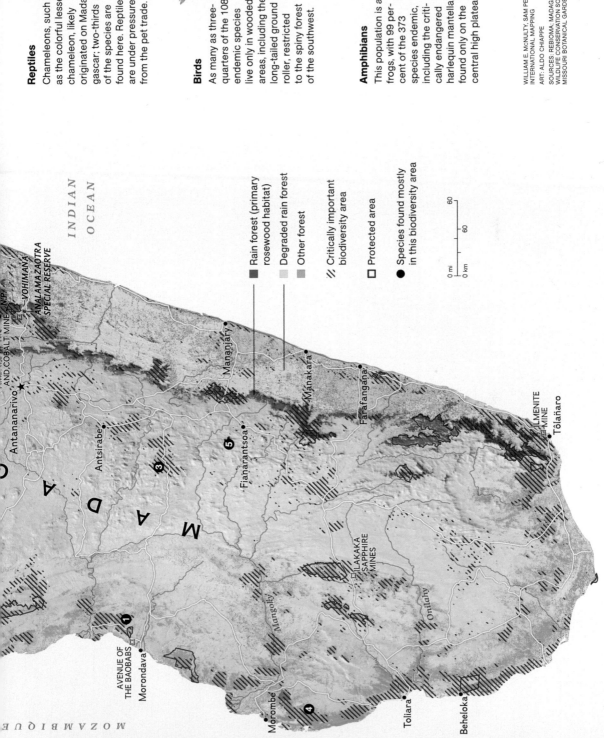

INDIAN OCEAN

MOZAMBIQUE

Antananarivo

Antsirabe

Fianarantsoa

Manakara

Manakara

Farafangana

Morondava

AVENUE OF THE BAOBABS

Morombe

Toliara

Beheloka

Tôlañaro

ILMENITE MINE

ILAKAKA SAPPHIRE MINES

Mangoky

Onilahy

ANALAMAZAOTRA SPECIAL RESERVE

VOHIMANA

AMBATOVY NICKEL AND COBALT MINE N.P.

MADAGASCAR

Legend

Rain forest (primary rosewood habitat)

Degraded rain forest

Other forest

Critically important biodiversity area

Protected area

● Species found mostly in this biodiversity area

0 mi 60
0 km 60

A PATH CUT for a pipeline serving the Ambatovy nickel mine slices into a species-rich forest. Ignoring the previous government's pledge to set aside 10 percent of the island for protected areas, the new leaders promote mining instead.

FOR SALE: four-month-old ring-tailed lemur, $50 or best offer. The owner poached the primate in a forest on the west coast. Hunters are increasingly catching lemurs, many of them endangered, to cash in on the illegal pet trade or to sell to restaurants like one in Sambava serving bush-meat stew.

stoic figures tugging a 400-pound log up some impossible gradient or down a waterfall or across quicksand-like bogs—a hard labor of biblical scale, except that these men are doing this for money. As is the man the pair would meet up with at the river, waiting to tie the log to a hand-crafted *radeau,* or raft, to help it float down the rapids ($25 a log). As is the pirogueman awaiting the radeau where the rapids subside ($12 a log). As is the park ranger whom the timber bosses have bribed to stay away ($200 for two weeks). As are police at checkpoints along the road to Antalaha ($20 an officer). The damage to the forest is far more than the loss of the precious hardwoods: For each dense rosewood log, four or five lighter trees are cut down to create the raft that will transport it down the river.

At a bend in the river, the pirogues pull up to shore. A man with a mustache squats in a tent, smoking a hand-rolled cigarette. His name is Dieudonne. He works with the middleman, the boss on the ground, entrusted by the timber baron to select the trees for cutting and oversee the logs from the riverbank to the transport trucks. There have been 18 trucks this morning. Thirty or so rosewood logs lie scattered around Dieudonne's tent. His cut is $12 a log. I ask him what he'll do with his money. He reflects for a moment.

"I'd like to buy a motorcycle," he says.

THE MAN WHO ENTRANCED the West with his pledges to usher in an eco-conscious era of *"Madagascar naturellement"* was Marc Ravalomanana, a former yogurt vendor who ascended to mayor of the capital city of Antananarivo, toppled the socialist President Ratsiraka, and formed the Tiako I Madagasikara (I Love Madagascar) political party in 2002. The president built roads and hospitals, distributed school uniforms, and symbolically cut the cord from the country's French colonialists by switching the currency from francs to Malagasy ariary. He also strengthened the ban on slash-and-burn agriculture (to no apparent effect, unfortunately), announced the Madagascar Action Plan to promote the country's biodiversity, and made a commitment to triple the size of Madagascar's

protected reserves. Utterances such as "our most important asset is our environment" were music to the green community's ears, and, as one environmentalist said, "I felt like we had a seat at the table."

Alas, different kinds of "action plans" were transpiring under the president's table: He reportedly confiscated harvested rosewood from the timber barons only to sell it for personal profit. He demanded, in the presence of reporters, a 10 percent cut of an oil company's exploration costs. As the president's wallet grew fatter, the purchasing power of his countrymen plummeted. Thousands of protesters stormed the presidential palace on February 7, 2009. They were met by gunfire, which left at least 30 dead. But a month later the military turned on Ravalomanana, who fled to Swaziland. Once in exile, he was convicted of confiscating city land for his family's business and using public funds to purchase a $60-million plane from Walt Disney's nephew.

The world community refused to recognize the new government, led by 34-year-old former Antananarivo mayor Andry Rajoelina. The World Bank, the UN, USAID and other donors withdrew funding, and Madagascar achieved the dubious distinction of being the first country to receive a $110-million U.S. Millennium Challenge Account grant and then, four years later, be kicked out of the program. Western countries issued travel advisories against going to Madagascar. Ravalomanana's green hand had been slapped away. The new government had no money to pay for enforcement of park regulations.

One group was plainly delighted by the turn of events. On March 17, 2009, the day Marc Ravalomanana signed his resignation papers, as many as 20,000 packed Antalaha's soccer stadium. Twelve zebu cattle were roasted, beer flowed in abundance, and villagers danced to live music all night. The tab was paid for by the area's 13 timber barons. The forest was unprotected.

It was theirs.

THE TIMBER BARON sits behind a desk of ebony, in a palisander chair, surrounded by palisander

LURED BY RUMORS of pink sapphires as big as a fist, many who flock to Ilakaka end up earning a few dollars on a shovel brigade (left and bottom right), lifting dirt out of an open-pit mine. While traders from Sri Lanka and Thailand take the best stones, Malagasy buyer Soaraza Arifeno (top right, wearing a sun mask made from root paste) selects second-tier gems for her African clients.

walls and ceiling and floor. Though his parents came over from China in the 1930s, and as he observes, "the Chinese people are crazy about rosewood," he himself was born near Antalaha and is partial to the russet brown color of palisander, a species closely related to the more beet-colored rosewood. His office is redolent with vanilla, owing to his adjacent warehouse, filled with bundles awaiting export. The growling of timber saws comes from his lumberyard, where piles of rosewood lie unhidden. Lean and muscular young men sit on benches outside the office door, where a note says, "People coming to pick up their paycheck must present their I.D."

His name is Roger Thunam, and it is widely believed that he is among the biggest rosewood businessmen in Madagascar. He is a compact, bespectacled man of middle age with distinctly Asian features, calmly self-possessed in the way of those who wield great power. The country's small population of Chinese émigrés are thoroughly assimilated into the community. Thunam is proof of this: He is a gregarious presence around Antalaha, a soft touch when a local peasant needs help paying for a funeral, not to mention a good man to see when gainful employment is sought. Still, despite the many fees paid up the timber chain—to the cutters, the draggers, the rafters, the piroguemen, the middlemen, the truck drivers and cops along the highway en route to the ports at Iharaña and Toamasina—the lion's share reverts to men like this one who, as he confesses, "can't remember when I was last in the forest."

"Thunam isn't a businessman—he's a trafficker," says one local official. "He cuts what isn't his. He's taken from the people's park. And now others think it's acceptable to take what's forbidden." Unsurprisingly, Thunam asserts otherwise. Born into the vanilla business, he expanded into timber 30 years ago. Since that time, he says, the government has issued him various permits.

Indeed, the government has lifted the ban on exporting rosewood when cyclones ravage the forest along the eastern coast of Madagascar, allowing trees damaged by the storms to be cut and traded. This fluctuating policy has allowed timber barons to stockpile illegal logs when the ban is in effect and then sell them as "salvaged" timber when the ban is temporarily lifted. The loophole only encourages further illegal cutting in the national parks—where the most rosewood can still be found.

Thunam insists he cuts only legal timber—though yes, his lumberyard is currently cluttered with rosewood logs, and he can explain this: "You wouldn't believe all of the men out there cutting. They're the same ones who've done slash and burn in the past. They've never been to school. They don't care about the next generation. They're the destroyers… But this lumber is already cut. If we don't buy it from them, someone else will."

He acknowledges that the rosewood-crazy Chinese are "the most important buyers." (A rosewood dining room set produced in China retails for upwards of $5,000.) And even when the new government allowed a temporary reversal of the ban to expire during the summer of 2009, the Chinese continued to place orders with Thunam for rosewood. To let his competitors have all that business would diminish him, he says. "In six months, we'd be very small."

The timber baron's wife, an ample middle-aged woman, enters the office and listens to the exchange. When her husband departs, she confesses, "I don't like to destroy the forests. I'd prefer to stop cutting and to just export what's already been cut. A few weeks ago I was on a plane, and I flew low over the forest. I could see the destruction. That's when I decided it should be stopped."

But how? Later I ask Antalaha's mayor, Risy Aimé. "To stop it is easy," he replies. "Go arrest 13 people"—referring to Roger Thunam and the other timber barons.

Every so often, the government has done just that, bringing charges against timber barons suspected of illegal trading. But the traders wield enormous power and have been able to take advantage of the chaotic legal status of logging. According to a report by Global Witness and the Environmental Investigation Agency, Thunam was one of only two barons (out of six known cases) found guilty of exporting rosewood; he was released from custody in 2008 after paying an

DESPITE THE MONEY PAID TO THE CUTTERS, THE RAFTERS, THE COPS, THE MIDDLEMEN— THE LION'S SHARE GOES TO THE TIMBER BARONS.

out-of-court settlement. Charged again in 2009, Thunam was found not guilty. The timber baron can once more be found behind his ebony desk, presiding over a humming lumberyard.

MY GUIDE IN MASOALA, a former park employee named Rabe, has been into the forest over a hundred times in the past decade. He keeps up a brisk and barefoot pace through a tangled, claustrophobic wilderness, seeing it with intimate familiarity. But to his surprise, something has changed since his last visit a few months before.

"No lemurs," he says. "They've disappeared."

The rosewood thieves are behind this. Weary of a rice-only diet, they have begun to lay traps. We learn of one team that captured 16 lemurs in a single day. Not all of them are being eaten on the spot. In the town of Sambava, just north of Antalaha, three restaurants feature lemurs on their menu, despite federal laws. In this way the rain forests of northeastern Madagascar are rapidly losing the red ruffed, the fork-marked, the greater dwarf, and the aye-aye. Lemurs are found in no other country on Earth, save the nearby Comoros islands.

"We don't want to conserve an empty forest, where the only thing you can come to see is trees," says primatologist Jonah Ratsimbazafy of the Durrell Wildlife Conservation Trust. For all of Madagascar's ecological richness, central to its multimillion-dollar tourist trade is its quintessential mascot, attested to by the thousands who visit the Analamazaotra Special Reserve. These bug-eyed, tree-dwelling primates fascinate not only because they are here and only here, but also because they are here in such diversity. Though virtually all 50 species of lemurs are polygamous, have luxurious tails, and many tend to grunt like pigs, there's also the black-and-white indri, which is monogamous, has no tail, and rocks the forest with spectral wails. Incredibly, scientists continue to discover new species of lemurs on the island. But each species is few in number, and in the meantime, five different lemurs inhabit the list of the world's 25 most endangered primates.

As yet, no national outpouring of sympathy for the lemur's plight has emerged. The Malagasy "should be proud of lemurs because Madagascar's the only place for them," says Ratsimbazafy. "But some people here don't know or care. The Malagasy who don't live near tourist areas think that lemurs are just for the *vazaha* [white people]—they don't see the benefits." In fact, although some tribes consider certain species of lemur to be sacred, the rather alarming-looking aye-aye, with its outsize eyes and ears, is believed by tribes in the north to be an evil omen and is therefore killed on the spot.

Such taboos have governed Malagasy conduct for centuries. They're admonitions from the ancestors, believed to linger on Earth as intermediaries to the afterlife and, therefore, to be heeded and appeased—sometimes, as I witnessed, through *famadihana*, a ceremony in which ancestors' bones are dug up, ceremonially wrapped in fresh white shrouds, and danced with around the tomb before being returned to the earth. In different tribes, it's fady to touch a chameleon or to talk about crocodiles or to eat pork or to work on Thursdays. Numerous fady prohibit the desecration of a mountain, a large boulder, a stand of trees, or even an entire forest—all evidence of a deep, if complicated, connection to the land and a spiritual investment in its good health. Nonetheless, the fady that tend to be heeded most reliably are those that do not collide with the Malagasy verity that it's better to die tomorrow.

"YOU SEE THAT BALD PATCH?" says Olivier Behra, pointing to a conspicuously deforested swath

ANCESTORS RECEIVE hands-on love during *famadihana,* a "turning the bones" reburial ceremony still popular in rural areas. Every five years or so, Jean Louis Rakotondrasoa (above) opens the family tomb to take the remains of relatives outside, where they are rewrapped in new shrouds and feted with music and dancing (below). Families save for years to pay for the feast (left).

ONLY FRAGRANT VANILLA pods pass a sniff test at an Antalaha warehouse, where workers check for whiffs of mold. Prices for vanilla, a leading export earner, have plunged due to global overproduction, pushing farmers into forests to hunt and chop.

amid acres of trees. "There's a guy over there who's been cutting. I'm trying to get him to stop."

"How do you propose to do that?" I ask.

Smiling, Behra says, "Employ him."

Behra's efforts represent an enlightened, if localized, solution to Madagascar's resource dilemma: Promote the immediate benefits of a vital forest to villagers. The Frenchman first came to Madagascar in 1987 on a UN project to save the unloved but seriously depleted crocodile population. Realizing that "if you give value to crocodiles, then people will become interested," he began to pay the locals to harvest crocodile eggs. Since 2000 Behra has been applying the same formula to the endangered forests of Madagascar through his NGO, Man and the Environment. In the woodlands of Vohimana a hundred miles east of the capital, Behra encountered a forest that had been halved over the previous four decades. Using the expertise of the locals, he cataloged 90 medicinal plants, then set up schemes to market them overseas. The French fragrance company Chanel became interested in extracts from Madagascan leaves like *marungi*. By 2007 the deforestation in Vohimana had ceased. Instead of hundreds of villagers slashing and burning, they're now collecting and selling leaves never thought to have economic value.

"I built myself a house here," says Behra. "The people see I'm not leaving tomorrow, so they can trust me." He's been a resourceful but unimposing presence. Recognizing that "you can't just take a lifelong woodcutter and expect to train him in agriculture," Behra persuaded the Madagascan government to allow the locals to continue to use a portion of the forest to harvest wood for domestic charcoal use. Having learned that there was a lemur hunter in the village, Behra employed the man as a guide for lemur-obsessed tourists. Another man who had made a living harvesting the forest's rare orchids is now the head of Behra's orchid conservatory. When Behra considered a project to farm the forest's wild pigs, which were destroying the cassava plantation he had set up, the Betsimisaraka tribesmen informed him that pigs were fady, and

"you have to respect that." He has persuaded Chanel to donate money for medical staff and school lunches in Vohimana.

"Working on a small scale the way Behra is doing may be more effective than these dreams of saving the whole forests," says Jean-Aimé Rakotoarisoa, for 30 years the director of the Museum of Art and Archaeology at the University of Antananarivo. "Most of the environmental programs say, Don't burn the forest because this is your future. But these people can't wait for the future. They're hungry now. You have to show the immediate benefit to the community."

That's a message getting through to a handful of large-scale resource extractors. Rakotoarisoa now serves as a consultant to the Ambatovy project, a $4.5-billion nickel and cobalt mining operation led by a foreign consortium and located near Olivier Behra's forest. The project, though controversial because it has not yet delivered on all of its promises, has taken care to avoid fady sites, compensate (and, where necessary, relocate) affected villagers, and continually engage with the community. These efforts aren't altruistic, Rakotoarisoa readily concedes. "For the sake of the company's image, they have to take care of the environmental and social concerns. They can't do business here if there's social protest."

On the southeastern tip of the island near Tôlañaro, the Anglo-Australian mining company Rio Tinto is attempting an ambitious good-neighbor policy to offset its $940-million project along the Indian Ocean coast extracting ilmenite, rich in titanium, a common ingredient in paints, paper, and plastic. The activity has involved gutting unique littoral forests containing 19 endemic species as well as medicinal plants and basket-weaving reeds. Still, in contrast to the timber barons several hundred miles up the coast, Rio Tinto is trying to preserve every single species. The company has set aside forestland for conservation, launched an agricultural training program, built a public seaport, and has plans to begin rehabilitating the land next year.

"We have high standards, and we'd like to influence other mining companies to be the

A FARMER AND HIS OXEN haul children to family rice plots near Morondava, along a path obscured during a flood. Madagascans are trying to figure out how best to survive in uncertain terrain.

same way," says Manon Vincelette, a forest engineer hired in 1996 to direct Rio Tinto's biodiversity program. Though the residents of Tôlañaro have a new road, new and renovated schools, and, in some cases, new jobs at the mine, local skepticism remains as to whether the foreign company is looking after any interest other than its own. "Rio Tinto is doing good things," says the ethnologist Jean-Aimé Rakotoarisoa. "But I've heard the rumors in that community—and from a social standpoint, rumor is more important than facts. You can't just deal with engineers and experts. There is no other way; you must know exactly the mind of the people."

THE ANTALAHA AIRPORT is small and wholly unadorned. Dogs and chickens poke around for scraps of food. Several dozen people await the incoming flight from Antananarivo. Through the doorway steps Roger Thunam, accompanied by his assistant. The timber baron walks from one side of the building to the other, shaking everyone's hands, hugging women, trading fond words.

Then he strolls outside and, until the arrival of the plane, leans contentedly against a fruit stand and drinks from a coconut with the other villagers—no different from the rest of them, a man of the people, one who knows their mind... and one who provides, at least for today. ☐

Perched on the tendril of a Passiflora plant, the egg of the Julia heliconian butterfly may be safe from hungry ants. This species lays its eggs almost exclusively on this plant's twisted vines.

DRYAS IULIA

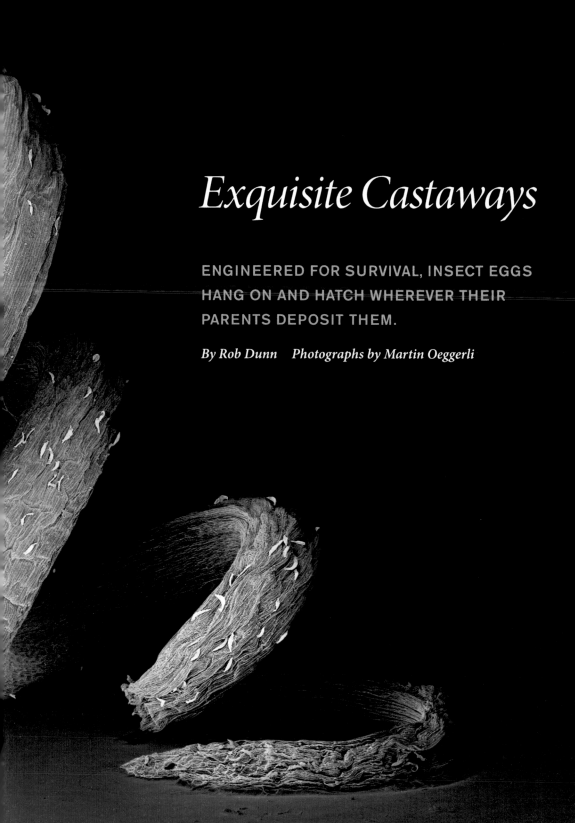

Exquisite Castaways

ENGINEERED FOR SURVIVAL, INSECT EGGS
HANG ON AND HATCH WHEREVER THEIR
PARENTS DEPOSIT THEM.

By Rob Dunn   Photographs by Martin Oeggerli

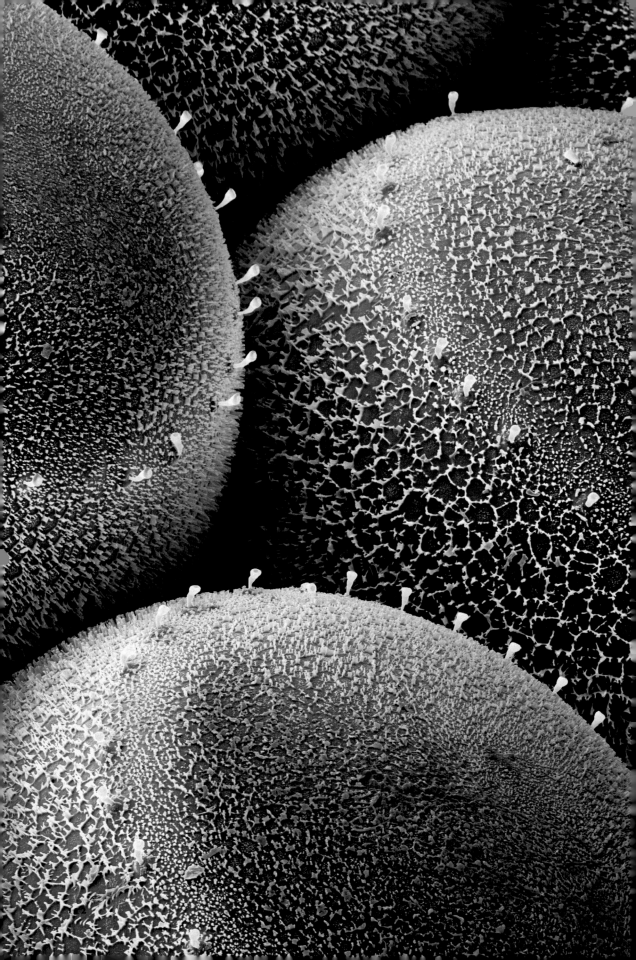

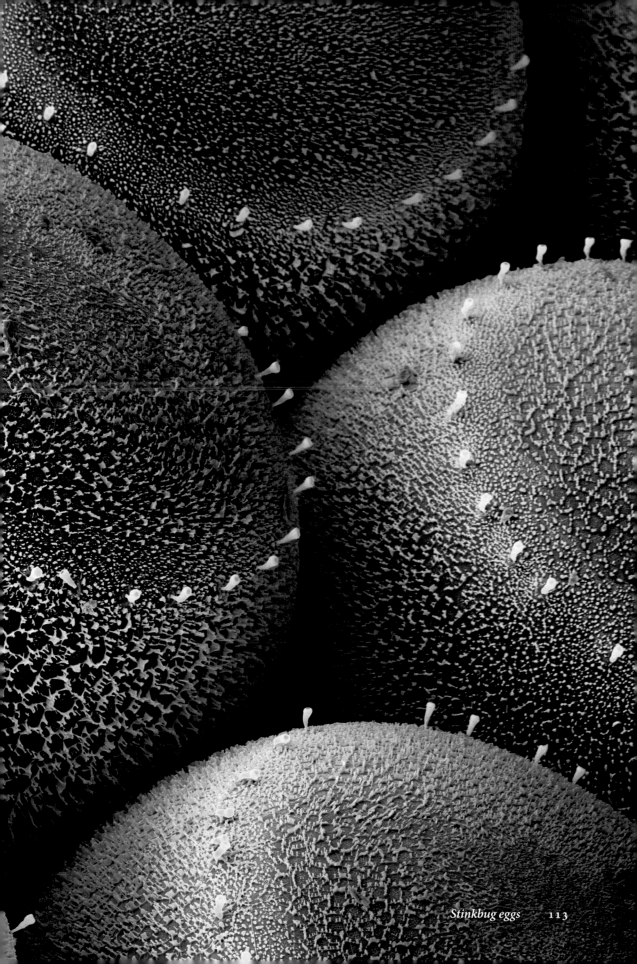

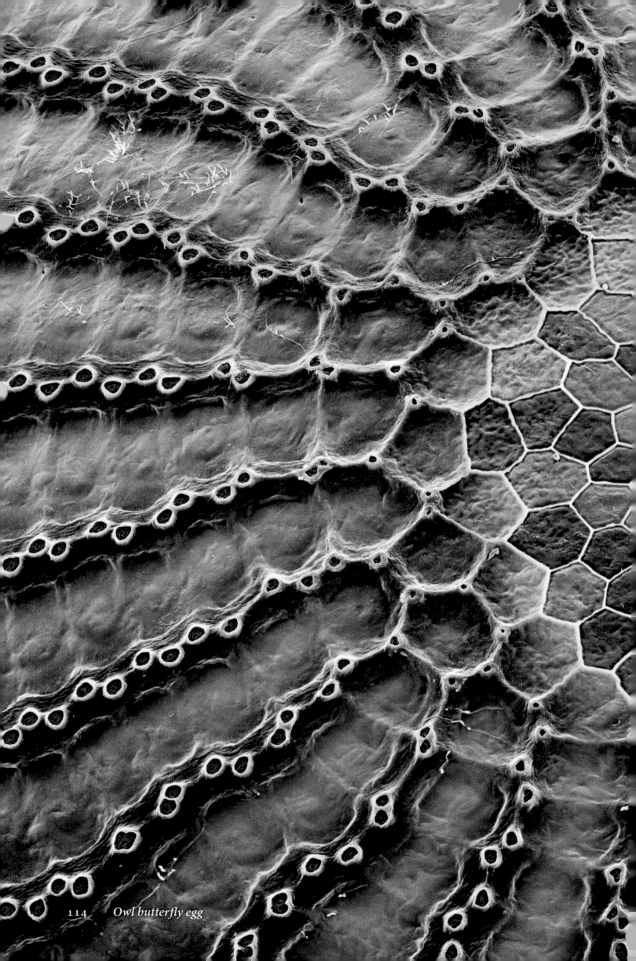

Owl butterfly egg

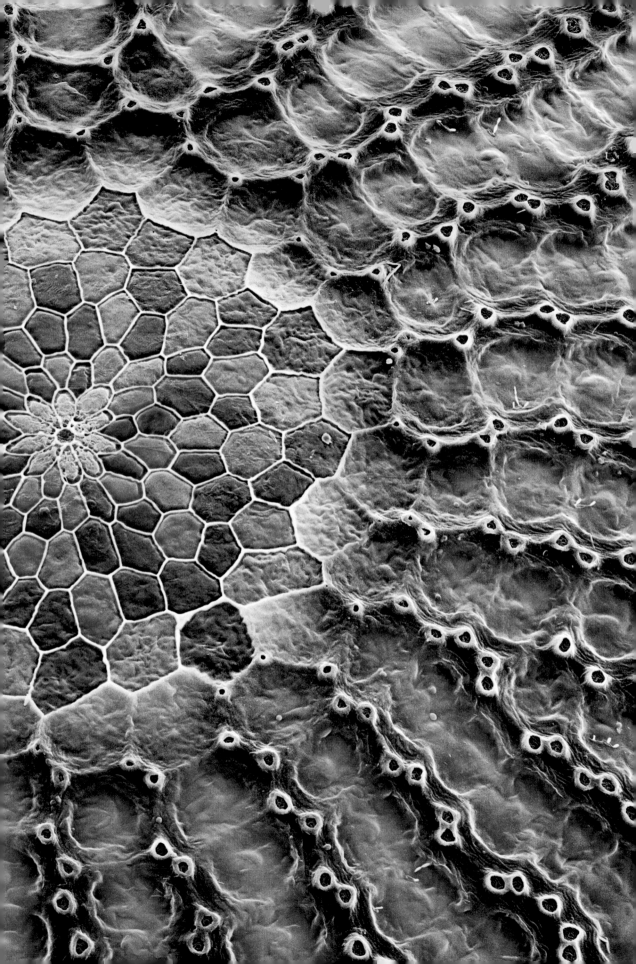

WE FOOL OURSELVES MOST DAYS.
WE IMAGINE THE EARTH TO BE OURS,
BUT IT BELONGS TO THEM. WE HAVE BARELY
BEGUN TO COUNT THEIR KINDS. NEW FORMS
TURN UP IN MANHATTAN, IN BACKYARDS, NEARLY
ANYTIME WE FLIP A LOG. NO TWO SEEM THE SAME.
THEY WOULD BE LIKE EXTRATERRESTRIALS AMONG
US, EXCEPT THAT FROM ANY DISTANCE WE ARE
THE ONES WHO ARE UNUSUAL, ALIEN TO
THEIR MORE COMMON WAYS OF LIFE.

As the vertebrate monsters have waxed and waned, the insects have gone on mating and hatching and, as they do, populating every swamp, tree, and patch of soil. We talk about the age of dinosaurs or the age of mammals, but since the first animal climbed onto land, every age has been, by any reasonable measure, the age of insects too. The Earth is salted with their kind.

We know, in part, what makes the insects different. Those other first animals tended to their young, as do most of their descendants, such as birds, reptiles, and mammals, which still bring their young food and fight to protect them. Insects, by and large, abandoned these ancient traditions for a more modern life.

Insects evolved hardened eggs and with them a special appendage, an ovipositor, which some use to sink their eggs into the tissue of Earth. Lift a stone and you will find them. Split a piece of wood, and they are there, but not only there. Birds struggle to find good places to nest, yet insects evolved the ability to make anything— wood, leaves, dirt, water, even bodies (especially bodies)—a nursery. If there is a single feature that has ensured insects' diversity and success, it is the fact that they can abandon their young nearly everywhere and yet have them survive— because of those eggs.

They began simply, smooth and round, but over 300 million years, insect eggs have become as varied as the places where insects reign. Some eggs resemble dirt. Others resemble plants. When you find them, you might not know what you are seeing at first. The forms are unusual and embellished with ornaments and apparatuses. Some eggs breathe through long tubes that they extend up through water. Others dangle from silky stalks. Still others drift in the wind or

PAGES 112-13: *Stinkbugs often lay their eggs in clumps. Individual eggs are glued not only to each other but also to the leaf on which they are left. The delicate projections may aid, like snorkels, in respiration.* PENTATOMIDAE

PAGES 114-15: *The mosaic pattern on an owl butterfly egg looks like a landing pad. At the center is a minute opening, called a micropyle, through which the sperm enters the egg.* CALIGO MEMNON

ride on the backs of flies. They are as colorful as stones, shaded in turquoises, slates, and ambers. Spines are common, as are spots, helices, and stripes. More than biology, their designs suggest the work of an artist left to obsess among tiny forms. They are natural selection's trillion masterpieces; inside each is an animal waiting for some cue to break free.

The basic workings of insect eggs, however, like the basics of any egg, are recognizable. The egg develops its shell while still inside the mother. There the sperm must find and swim through an opening at one end of the egg, the micropyle. Sperm wait inside the mother for this chance, sometimes for years. One successful sperm, wearied but victorious, fertilizes each egg, and this union produces the undifferentiated beginnings of an animal nestled inside a womblike membrane. Here eyes, antennae, mouth parts, and all the rest form. As they do, the creature respires using the egg's aeropyles, through which oxygen diffuses in and carbon dioxide out. That all of this occurs in a structure typically no larger than a grain of raw sugar is simultaneously beyond belief and ordinary. This is, after all, the way in which most animals ever to have lived on Earth had their start.

What you see on these pages are the eggs of a few small branches of the insect tree of life. Among them are those of some butterflies that face extraordinary travails to defend themselves against predators and, sometimes, against plants on which they are laid. Some passionflowers transform parts of their leaves into shapes that resemble butterfly eggs; mother butterflies, seeing the "eggs," move on to other plants to deposit their babies. Such mimics are

Rob Dunn and Martin Oeggerli worked together on the story about pollen in the December 2009 issue.

imperfect, but fortunately so is butterfly vision.

Eggs must also somehow escape having the eggs of another type of insect, parasitoids, laid inside of them. Parasitoid wasps and flies use their long ovipositors to thrust their eggs into the eggs and bodies of other insects. Roughly 10 percent of all insect species are parasitoids. It is a well-rewarded lifestyle, punished only by the existence of hyperparasitoids, which lay their eggs inside the bodies of parasitoids while they are inside the bodies or eggs of their own hosts. Many butterfly eggs and caterpillars eventually turn into wasps as a consequence of this theater of life. Even the dead and preserved eggs shown here are likely to hold mysteries. Inside some are young butterflies, but inside others may be wasps or flies that have already eaten their first supper and, of course, their last.

Every so often, and against all odds, a group of insects has regressed a little and decided to care more actively for its young. Here and there we see the evidence. Dung beetles roll dung balls for their babies. Carrion beetles roll bodies. And then there are the roaches, some of which carry their newborn nymphs on their backs. The eggs of these insects have become featureless and round again, like lizard eggs, and in so doing also become more vulnerable and in need of care, like our own young. Yet they survive. Perhaps they are the vanguard of what will come next, the next kingdom beginning to rise. Though perhaps not. Recently I watched a dung beetle rolling a ball, and the ball looked like a rising sun. Above that beetle was a fly trying to lay an egg inside the beetle's head.

Insects have been cracking out of eggs for hundreds of millions of years. It is happening now, all around you. If you listen, you can almost hear the crumbling of the shells as tiny feet, six at a time, push into the world. ☐

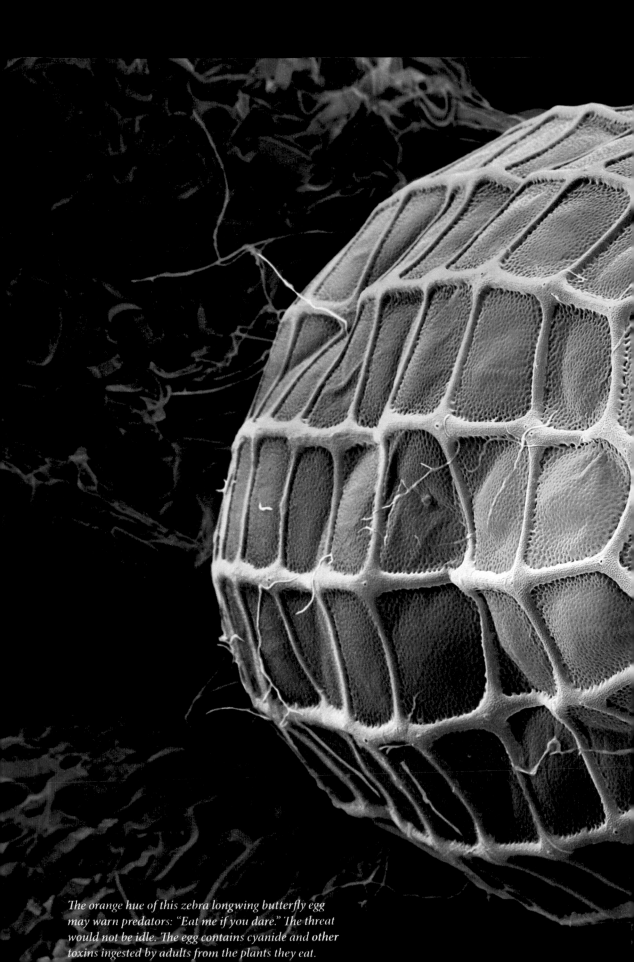

The orange hue of this zebra longwing butterfly egg
may warn predators: "Eat me if you dare." The threat
would not be idle. The egg contains cyanide and other
toxins ingested by adults from the plants they eat.

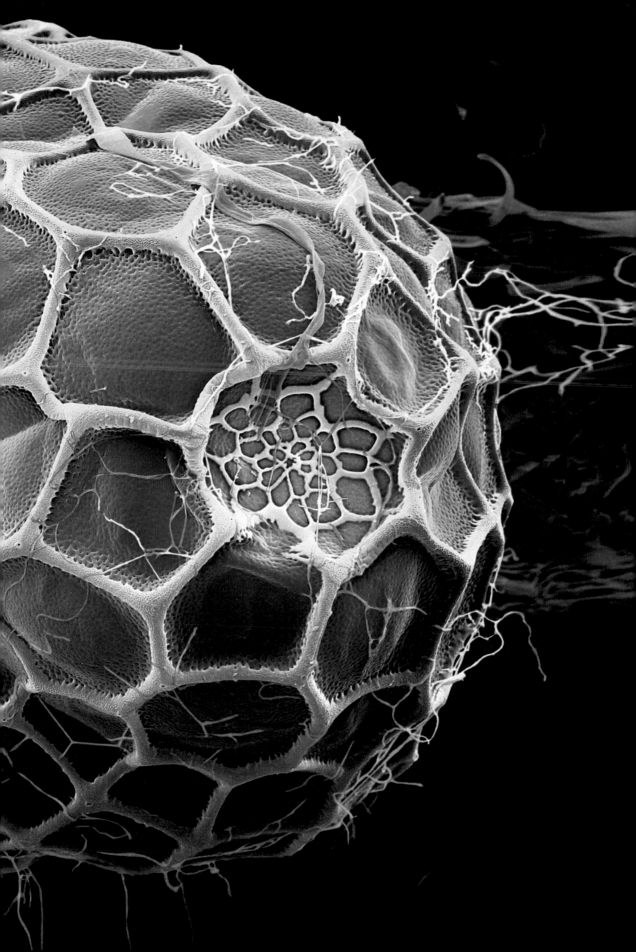

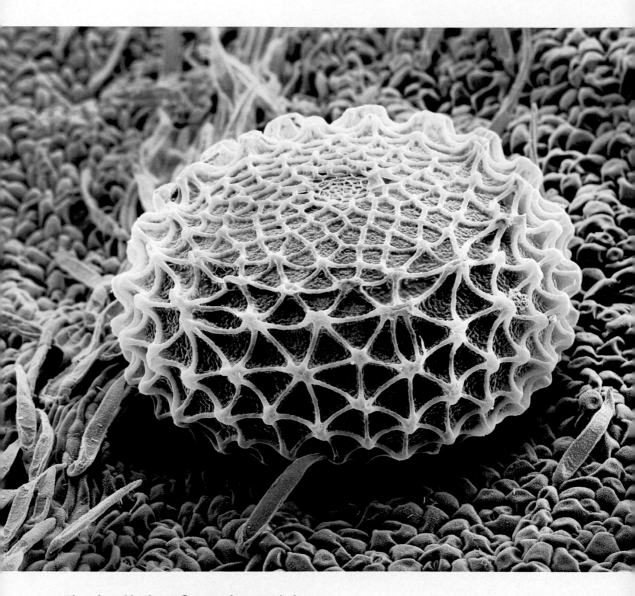

The Adonis blue butterfly is rare because it's choosy.
It lays its eggs (like the one above) only on horseshoe
vetch, a European perennial. What's more, it looks for
patches cropped by rabbits that allow easy landing.

LYSANDRA BELLARGUS

The eggs in this story range in diameter from 0.7 to 2 millimeters. The images were made with a
scanning electron microscope, which uses beams of electrons to trace the surfaces of objects.
The resulting black-and-white images were then colored to reflect the eggs' natural appearance.

PHOTOGRAPHIC COVERAGE PRODUCED IN COOPERATION WITH PRÜFTECHNIK URI AND SCHOOL OF APPLIED SCIENCES, FHNW

The red band signals a chemical reaction that follows fertilization. Inside the egg is the germ of a blue morpho, one of the world's largest butterflies, with a wingspan of five to eight inches.

MORPHO PELEIDES

Year-old "glass" eels hole up in Maine's Pemaquid River.

They spend decades in rivers and lakes, then
cross oceans and spawn in secret.

MYSTERY TRAVELERS *eels*

At dusk, lights guide Yvonne Carey (far left) and daughter Genna as they dip eels from Nova Scotia's East River and store them in a blue-topped bag. Licensed to fish nine rivers, the Careys truck their catch home to holding tanks to await live shipment to Asia.

a s a kid, I encountered eels more often in crossword puzzles or Scrabble (a good way to unload *e*'s) than in the wilds near my Connecticut home. But in the flesh, when my friends and I caught them by mistake on fishing outings, they were alien and weird, unnameable things—snakes, maybe, or what?—and we were afraid to retrieve our hooks from their mouths.

One day an old man casting nearby told us they were fish. I knew that if this was true, eels were fish like no others.

For much of my life I had little occasion to pay attention to eels. Then six years ago, while heading down Route 17 in the Catskills of New York State on a cold November day, I decided to follow a sign that said, "Delaware Delicacies, Smokehouse." Past the Cobleskill quarry, down a sinuous dirt road through a shadowy hemlock forest, I came to a small tar-paper shack with a silver smokestack, perched on a high bank overlooking the East Branch of the Delaware River. A man with a pointy white beard and a ponytail, who resembled a wood imp, hopped from behind the plywood door of the smokehouse. His name was Ray Turner.

Every summer when the river is low, Turner—slippery, resilient, and a bit mysterious himself—refurbishes the V-shaped stone walls of a weir that funnels water through a wooden rack designed to trap fish. It takes him the better part of four months to finish the work, in preparation for the eel run that occurs during just two nights in September, around the dark time of the new moon, when maturing eels swim downstream toward the ocean. The run often corresponds with floods brought on by storms during hurricane season, when the sky is at its blackest and the river at its highest. As Rachel Carson observed, the eel is "a lover of darkness."

We paddled in a canoe upstream from Turner's house toward the weir. "There's Baldy," he said, pointing to a bald eagle circling low, keeping an eye on the rack, looking to snag any fish before Turner did. In this broad valley, reminiscent of a Hudson River school painting, the weir made an impressive piece of land art. Turner spoke of it in metaphorical terms. "This is the womb," he said, as we perched on the rack. "Those are the legs." He gestured toward the stone breakwaters stretching diagonally on either side of the river. "You see? It's a woman. All the river's life comes here."

When the September run is good, Turner can take up to 2,500 eels. "Every year I let the biggest girl back in the river," he said. (Assuming the eel is a female and that she makes it out to sea to spawn, she will lay up to 30 million eggs.) Turner hot smokes his eels and sells them to passersby, as well as to restaurants and retailers, earning him up to $20,000 a year. "I consider the eels to be the best quality protein in my line—a very unique flavor of fish, applewood smoke, and a momentary

Ray Turner stirred the water, agitating

lingering of dark, fall honey. All the fish I smoke, trout and salmon, are farm raised, except the eels. The eels are wild. They're like free-range."

Back at the smokehouse, Turner showed me the two concrete-block chambers where the eels—dressed and brined in salt, brown sugar, and local honey—are hung on rods. Behind each chamber is a 55-gallon-drum stove with a door on the front and a chimney hole with two pipes in the back. Once the fire is going in the stove, Turner directs the heat and smoke into the chamber, and the eels are cooked at 160 to 180 degrees Fahrenheit for a minimum of four hours.

He ushered me through the back door, past

BY JAMES PROSEK   PHOTOGRAPHS BY DAVID DOUBILET

neat stacks of hand-split applewood, to a wooden tank, like a giant wine cask cut in half, covered in moss and dripping water through its swollen slats. I peered over the chicken wire around the rim into a clear pool. Turner stirred the water with a net, agitating some 500 silvery eels, most about as big around as a dollar coin and up to three feet long. They were lithe and sensuous—just magical.

FRESHWATER EELS, OF THE GENUS *Anguilla*, are ancient fishes. They began evolving more than 50 million years ago, branching into 16 species and three subspecies. Most migratory fish, such as salmon and shad, are anadromous, spawning in fresh water and living as adults in salt water. The freshwater eel is one of the few fishes that do the opposite, spawning in the ocean and spending their adulthood in lakes, rivers, and estuaries—a life history known as catadromy. In general, female eels are found upstream in river systems, while males stay in the estuaries. Eels may spend decades in rivers before returning to the ocean to spawn, after which they die. No one has ever been able to witness freshwater eels spawning, and for eel biologists, solving this eel-reproduction mystery remains a kind of holy grail.

Italian biologists watched one in a tank metamorphose into an eel.

Eels are relentless in their effort to return to their oceanic womb. I can tell you this from personal experience because I've tried to keep them in a home aquarium. The morning after the first night of my attempt, I found eels slithering around the floor of my kitchen and living room. After securing a metal screen over the tank with heavy stones, I was able to contain them, but soon they were rubbing themselves raw against the screen. Then one died trying to escape via the filter outflow. When I screened the outflow, eels banged their heads against the glass until they had what appeared to be seizures and died. That's when I stopped trying to keep eels.

They're wondrous in their ability to move. They show up in lakes and ponds and postholes with no visible connection to the sea, leaving the inquisitive shaking their heads. On wet nights eels have been known to cross land from a pond to a river by the thousands, using each other's moist bodies as a bridge. Young eels have been seen climbing moss-covered vertical walls. In New Zealand it's common for cats to bring eels to the doorsteps of farmhouses, having caught them in grassy paddocks.

some 500 eels, about as big around as a dollar coin and up to three feet long. They were lithe and sensuous—just magical.

In biology class we were told that the eels we caught in creeks and ponds had emerged from eggs suspended in the ocean, specifically the Sargasso Sea, the southwestern part of the clockwise gyre in the North Atlantic—an idea that required more faith than imagination. We know that freshwater eels reproduce in the ocean because larvae have been found drifting near the surface thousands of miles from any shore. Eel larvae—tiny, transparent creatures with thin heads, bodies shaped like willow leaves, and outward pointing teeth—were thought to be a separate species of fish until 1896, when two

"How many animals are there that live in such diverse habitats?" David Doubilet mused while photographing eels in New Zealand, knee-deep in a spring-fed creek, watercress dangling from his mask and snorkel. "Here we have a fish that is born in the deepest, darkest depths of the ocean, and yet here you have them in a farm paddock with cows."

French farmers in Normandy say that eels will leave rivers on spring nights and find their way to vegetable patches to feed on peas. That's a fable, but eels are one of the only fishes that will emerge from the water to take offerings of

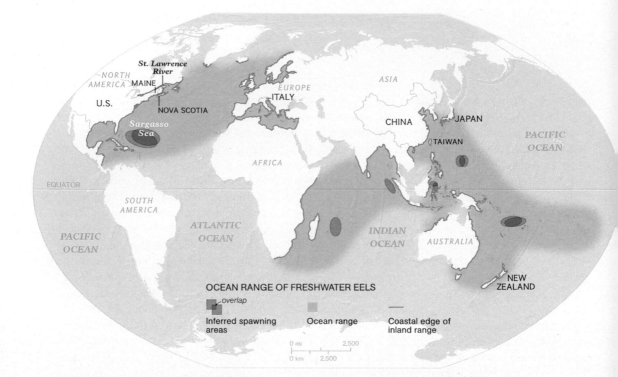

Map labels:

St. Lawrence River
NORTH AMERICA
MAINE
U.S.
NOVA SCOTIA
Sargasso Sea
EUROPE
ITALY
ASIA
CHINA
JAPAN
TAIWAN
PACIFIC OCEAN
AFRICA
EQUATOR
SOUTH AMERICA
ATLANTIC OCEAN
PACIFIC OCEAN
INDIAN OCEAN
AUSTRALIA
NEW ZEALAND

OCEAN RANGE OF FRESHWATER EELS

overlap

Inferred spawning areas

Ocean range

Coastal edge of inland range

0 mi   2,500
0 km   2,500

From Sea to Stream

Scientists know where some of the 16 freshwater eel species and three subspecies spawn, but no one has ever reported seeing eel reproduction in the wild. Larval eels ride ocean currents to lagoons, estuaries, rivers, and lakes. Many eels—almost exclusively females—move far inland. Years or even decades later adult eels return home by unknown routes to spawn and die.

food—canned mackerel or dog food—on river-banks. I've observed them doing this at sacred Maori eel-feeding sites in New Zealand. Under normal circumstances, an eel's diet is quite varied—everything from aquatic insects and fish to mussels and other eels.

Adaptability aside, the migrations millions of adult eels make from rivers across oceans must be among the greatest unseen journeys of any creature on the planet, spanning thousands of miles. Along the way they face a long list of dangers: hydroelectric dams, river diversions, pollution, disease, predation (by striped bass, beluga whales, and cormorants, among others), and increasingly, fishing by humans. Now, with climate change, another potential disaster looms: shifts in ocean currents that may confound eels during their migrations. Regrettably, although sublime in the eyes of some, the eel is not likely to be the poster child for a conservation movement anytime soon.

FROM ARISTOTLE TO PLINY THE ELDER, Izaak Walton to Carl Linnaeus, naturalists put forward various theories as to how eels came to be: that the young emerged from the mud, that eels multiplied by rubbing themselves against rocks, that they were born from a particular dew that falls in May and June, that they bear live young. One problem was that no one could identify sperm or eggs in eels. Over a 40-year period in the late 1700s, at the famous eel fishery at Comacchio, Italy, more than 152 million adult migratory eels were caught and cleaned, not one of which was found carrying eggs. No one could say for sure whether eels even had gender, because no one could identify their reproductive organs. (It turns out that the sex organs of eels become enlarged with eggs and sperm only after the adults leave the mouths of rivers for their oceanic spawning grounds and disappear from sight.)

In the late 1800s in Trieste, Italy, a medical student named Sigmund Freud was assigned to

LISA R. RITTER, NGM STAFF; MAGGIE SMITH
SOURCE: MICHAEL J. MILLER, ATMOSPHERE AND OCEAN RESEARCH INSTITUTE, UNIVERSITY OF TOKYO

investigate the testes of the male eel, postulated to be loops of white matter festooning the body cavity. (Freud's paper on eels was his first published work.) This was confirmed in 1897, when a sexually mature male eel was caught in the Strait of Messina.

In 1904 Johannes Schmidt, a young Danish oceanographer and biologist, got a job aboard the *Thor,* a Danish research vessel, studying the breeding habits of food fishes such as cod and herring. One day that spring, a larva of the European eel, *Anguilla anguilla,* showed up in one of the expedition's trawls west of the Faroe Islands. Was it possible that eels living in the creeks of Denmark spawned way out in the middle of the Atlantic Ocean?

A year earlier Schmidt had made what would end up being an auspicious betrothal to the heiress of the Carlsberg Brewery, a Danish company that donated generously to marine research. Outfitted with schooners capable of ocean crossings, he amassed data showing that the farther from the European coast, the smaller the eels. Schmidt asserted that eels must spawn in the southwestern part of the North Atlantic, in the Sargasso Sea. "No other instance is known

Yoshiaki Miyamoto hooked just one eel on his morning stint on Lake Biwa, near Kyoto. The Japanese believe eels boost energy and cool the blood in summer; local stocks are in decline.

among fishes of a species requiring a quarter of the circumference of the globe to complete its life history," he wrote in 1923. "Larval migrations of such extent and duration…are altogether unique in the animal kingdom."

After Schmidt's death in 1933, some scientists cast doubt on his Sargasso proposition. They showed that he had concealed certain data to make his case more plausible, and they questioned how he could say with any certainty that this was the only eel breeding ground, since he hadn't witnessed an actual hatching and had barely looked for eels anywhere else. Yet such criticism does little to diminish the profound story of eels he conveyed, which still appears to be true.

In 1991 an expedition headed by Katsumi Tsukamoto of the Atmosphere and Ocean Research

James Prosek celebrates eels in a book for HarperCollins, out in October. David Doubilet photographed clownfish for the January issue.

New Zealand's longfin eels are giants, some topping six feet and 80 pounds, that can live for decades. Traditional Maori prize them as guardians of sacred spaces—and as dinner. These females at South Island's Willowbank Wildlife Reserve could be 30 years old.

Institute of the University of Tokyo that included Michael Miller, then a graduate student at the University of Maine, made another breakthrough. On a dark night in the Pacific Ocean west of Guam, the team found hundreds of larvae of the Japanese eel, *Anguilla japonica,* within days of their hatching, thus locating the spawning area of this species for the first time. Nineteen years later Tsukamoto and Miller are still searching the oceans for spawning eels.

When I met Miller in his Tokyo office, he ruefully acknowledged that he and Tsukamoto have come tantalizingly close to finding the parents of Japanese eel hatchlings. But, he said, "you could be 50 meters away and not find anything. It's an issue of scale—the ocean is huge. To get where eels are spawning, it's statistically very low probability. Almost impossible. You'd have to be very lucky." What's more, he added, every year that he and Tsukamoto go looking, they seem to run afoul of the elements. "I can't remember a single eel cruise when there hasn't been a typhoon that's caused us to change course. It's almost like Poseidon is trying to keep the eels secret."

THAT'S THE GREATEST BEAUTY I find in eels: the idea of a creature whose very life beginnings can remain hidden from humans. It makes it all the harder for me to accept the thought that we may lose this creature before its life picture can be completed. Populations of American, European, and Japanese eels are all declining, some precipitously. As John Casselman, a biologist at Queen's University in Kingston, Ontario, told me, "It is truly a crisis. A crisis of concern."

In November 2004 two brothers, Doug Watts, a freelance journalist who lives in Augusta, Maine, and Tim Watts, a janitor at a college in Easton, Massachusetts, petitioned the U.S. Fish and Wildlife Service (FWS) to list the American eel, *Anguilla rostrata,* as a threatened, or even endangered, species. They were motivated by Casselman's documentation of the collapse of eel populations in the upper St. Lawrence River: From the mid-1980s to the middle of the past decade, the number of juveniles there fell by almost 100 percent. The region encompassing the upper St. Lawrence River system and Lake Ontario and its tributaries is North America's largest eel nursery, where it is thought that female eels alone once made up 50 percent of the inshore fish biomass.

One problem for the eels was the earlier construction of the Beauharnois and Moses-Saunders hydroelectric dams, which have blocked their migrations to and from the upper St. Lawrence River system and Lake Ontario. Even if a young eel, aided by fish ladders, succeeds in getting upriver, when she comes downriver as an adult, she may be sucked into a dam's electricity-generating turbines. "Some eels come out with their skin pulled off, like a sock off your foot," Doug Watts told me. The bigger the eel, the greater the danger. In New Zealand, where longfins grow to six feet or more, turbines mean certain death.

In February 2007 the FWS announced in a 30-page report that listing American eels under the Endangered Species Act was "not warranted," in part because some eels have been found to spend their whole lives in salty estuaries. "The findings basically said that eels don't need freshwater habitat to survive," Watts said, throwing up his hands in exasperation. "That's like saying bald eagles don't need trees to nest in—they can

In one Maori myth, eels come from the

use telephone poles." Because eels have always been ubiquitous and abundant, Watts says, no one seems to believe they could ever go extinct. "That's what they said about cod as recently as the 1990s, when stocks were collapsing. 'There's no way you can fish out cod—that's insane!' they said." He paused. "You can only beat an animal so hard before it finally just gives up."

EELS THAT SURVIVE DAMS may not survive Earth's top predator. The international trade, driven largely by Japan's appetite for grilled eel, called *kabayaki,* is a multibillion-dollar industry. In Japan, eel is believed to increase one's stamina in the heat, and Doyo Ushi No Hi, eel day, usually falls in late July. During that month in 2009 at Tokyo's famed Tsukiji seafood market, more than 111,500 pounds of fresh eel were sold. Eel is almost always eaten in eel-only restaurants, because of the difficulty in cleaning and cooking the fish. It is never served raw: The blood contains a neurotoxin that's neutralized when cooked or hot smoked. (A tiny amount of eel-blood serum injected into a rabbit causes instant convulsions and death.)

The eel is grilled on bamboo skewers over a hot wood fire, repeatedly dipped in water, and returned to the fire to steam the meat. Then it's glazed with a sauce of soy, mirin (sweet rice wine), and sugar and sprinkled with *sansho*, mountain pepper. This dish, most often a single eel split and splayed over a bed of rice in a black, lacquered box with a red interior, is called *unaju*. No part of the fish goes to waste. The liver is served in a soup, and the spine is deep-fried and eaten like a cracker. Though it may be part of Japan's food folklore, it is said that in Tokyo the eel is filleted along the back to avoid mimicking the samurai warrior's ritual knife-in-the-belly suicide. In Kyoto, where there were fewer samurai, it is filleted along the belly. Kyoto

market usually involves catching babies—called glass eels because of their transparency—when they arrive in fresh water from the ocean and shipping them to warehouse-style farms in China for fattening up. The trade remains dependent on the capture of wild fish because no one has figured out how to reproduce eels profitably in captivity.

IN THE U.S. DURING THE 1970S, when aquaculture farms were burgeoning in China, eel fishing to supply the Asian market went on pell-mell from January through June in every East Coast state. Pat Bryant of Nobleboro, Maine, was one of the first in the state to catch glass eels for export to China. By day she ran a hairdressing salon in the coastal town of Damariscotta, and at night, to make a little extra money, she went down to the mouth of the Pemaquid River to check her nets.

The commercial operation in Maine grew explosively from the mid-1980s to the mid-1990s, when the more than 1,500 fishers with permits could each make several thousand dollars a night at the dock for their catch. People began stealing and vandalizing nets and pulling .357 Magnums to stake out or preserve fishing territories. In one creek, fishermen had a net called the green

sky, having fallen when the heavens became too hot. On Earth, some say, the movements of eels make the rivers flow.

people say that the women in their city have such beautiful skin because they eat plenty of eel. Indeed, the meat is high in vitamins A and E, and because of its high concentration of omega-3 fatty acids, it has been found to help prevent type 2 diabetes.

An eel served in a restaurant in Manhattan may have hatched in the Atlantic Ocean, been netted in a river mouth in the Basque region of France, flown to Hong Kong, raised at a farm in nearby Fujian or Guangdong Provinces, cleaned, grilled, and packaged in factories near the farms, and finally flown to New York City. Readying eels for

monster. "It went clear across the river," Bryant said in her raspy voice, ashing her cigarette in a scallop shell. "It was a goddamn fiasco." She and a few others appealed to the state, "just out of our own preservation." Today the allowable eel take in Maine—the state with the most active fishery—is restricted to a few locations and a short season, from March 22 to May 31.

In 1997 record-low catches of prized Japanese glass eels sent prices soaring—a single kilo (2.2 pounds), about 5,000 of them, sold for as much as $16,500, making eel more valuable at the time than gold. When the supply of Japanese

Black eyes and red hearts dot glass eels scooped into a tank from Maine's Damariscotta River. This batch, worth some $400 a pound, is bound for China. Eeling in the U.S. is heavily regulated; Maine is one of the few states allowing the export of glass eels.

Eels cook over a beech and oak fire at Dutchman Alex Koelewijn's smokehouse. They melt in your mouth like fine chocolate, he says. "It's the oily and smoky taste that gives the most joy."

glass eels crashed, the price for American glass eels briefly increased tenfold—the eel gold rush, as Bryant calls it. Japanese connoisseurs weren't happy. "American eels are not as tasty," Shoichiro Kubota, who runs a 120-year-old eel restaurant in the Akihabara district of Tokyo, told me. (His father was eel handler to Emperor Hirohito.) "Even the French eels are not as good—like American cherries. Not as tasty. We like our native things."

Bryant buys glass eels from fishermen up and down the Maine coast and babysits them in tanks near her home until they're ready for shipment from Boston to Hong Kong, live, in plastic bags filled with oxygenated water and packed in foam containers. Until recently, Jonathan Yang, a dealer from Taiwan, was the middleman between Bryant and eel farmers in China and Taiwan, buying eels from her by the kilo and selling them by the piece, or individual eel. He paid cash, typically wiring a million dollars to a bank in Maine at the end of the season.

When the selling was good, Yang doubled his money, but more often than not he had to accept a modest profit. "This is a very big business, very risky," he said. If the price for adult eels fell during the 14 to 18 months it took to raise a glass eel for market, his Chinese buyer could go bankrupt. "One year the farm sells high—they all drive Mercedes-Benzes," Yang said. "Next year price falls—they're riding bicycles."

Before he went into eels, Yang was in the lucrative business of selling shark fins in China for soup. He says he quit when he saw dolphins, caught accidentally on longline hooks, being dragged aboard ship, beaten to death, and thrown back into the sea. "When they take the dolphins on the ship," Yang said, "you know they're weeping—you can see the tears." He put his hand over his heart. "When I look at eels, I feel good. When they move, they look very nice."

LIKE JONATHAN YANG, I get a good feeling from eels. The times I've spent with them, especially during the fall migration, have pulsed with energy. Standing in Ray Turner's weir on a cool September night on the eve of the new moon, watching veinlike ropes of eels fill his womb of wood and stone, I could almost believe the Maori's yarns about encounters they've had with the *taniwha*—the water guardian or monster. For many indigenous people throughout the Polynesian Islands, the eel is a god that replaces the archetypal snake in creation myths, an important source of food, and an erotic symbol—the word many islanders use for eel, *tuna,* is synonymous with "penis." In one Maori myth, eels come from the sky, having fallen when the heavens became too hot and inhospitable for them. On Earth, some Maori say, the movements of eels make the rivers flow. The eel is integral to everything.

We allow ourselves to believe we can understand nature by organizing and explaining it through systems of taxonomy and computerized studies of genes and DNA, fitting everything into neat categories. With each passing year, researchers peer deeper into the hidden lives of eels; in 2006 and again in 2008, scientists released adult eels from the west coasts of Ireland and France outfitted with pop-up tags, hoping to track them to the Sargasso Sea. But "knowledge," as we amass it (ever available, at our fingertips), can hinder imagination and the wonder that can come from our own observation. Eels—with their simplicity of form, their preference for darkness, their gracefulness—have helped me embrace the unnameable and get to the essence of experience, that which cannot be cataloged or quantified. They have been my way back.

The immense pressures on eels today will test their ability to adapt and survive. A Maori bush guide named Daniel Joe spoke of the staying power of eels as we sat by a campfire on the Waipunga River. "He's an old fish, and he's absolutely relentless," Joe said. "The eel is *morehu,*" a survivor. "I think they will be there till the end of the world as we know it."

I hope he's right. ☐

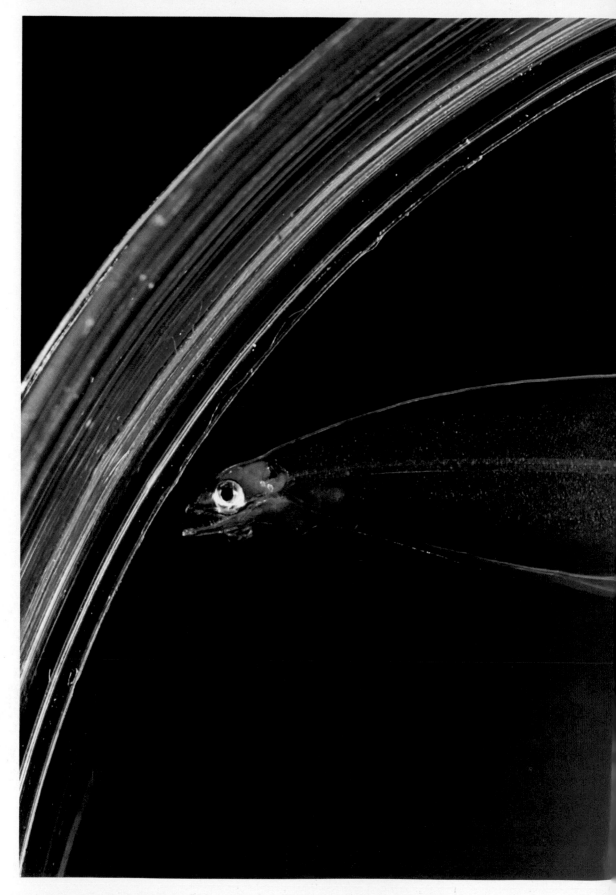

A weeks-old eel larva in a petri dish glows under blue light. In a recent breakthrough, Japanese scientists raised eels hatched in the lab until they spawned. Though there is much still to learn, captive breeding could someday give wild stocks a reprieve.

Villagers carry Moimango, mummified half a century ago, up to his cliff-niche perch. His son, current "big man" Gemtasu

...ouching), hopes to be mummified someday too.

Mastering Mummy Science

Mummy expert Ronald Beckett is helping a South Pacific culture revive a disappearing ancient tradition.

I LOVE MEETING NEW MUMMIES. As a biomedical specialist, I've worked on hundreds of them over the past 15 years, everywhere from Thailand to Peru. Normally I study them in labs and museums, but in Koke, a village in Papua New Guinea, where I started working in 2008, mummies are a daily part of the living culture. There's a physical, emotional, human connection with them that's unique.

The first time I visited Koke, I was greeted by a man in tapa cloth with a cassowary bone through his nose. He was holding a bow and arrow. I smiled and

PACIFIC OCEAN

INDONESIA PAPUA NEW GUINEA
Koke ● Port ★ Moresby

0 mi 400
0 km 400

AUSTRALIA

thought, Wow, neat! In fact, he was issuing me a warrior's challenge: Why have you come? "I'm here to work on the mummy called Moimango," I said. "I'm here to examine and restore him so he can sit on the cliff for many years to come." The next thing I knew, the man was rubbing his nose against mine. He'd accepted my answer. Locking noses makes an official statement of welcome.

It was easier when I met Gemtasu, head of the Anga people of Koke. Thanks to photographer Ulla Lohmann's introduction, I had come at his request. Moimango was his father. He'd been a great warrior and shaman, and some 50 years ago he'd returned to the village from a hunt or a battle complaining of having the "short wind." He lay down by a fire and died. In keeping with tradition, Gemtasu *(Continued)*

PHOTO: ULLA LOHMANN. NGM MAPS

Ronald Beckett (at right) inspects the carcass of a forest pig villagers used to practice mummification techniques. The smoke, he found, is extremely acidic, inhibiting enzymes that contribute to decomposition.

and other family members mummified his body in a special smoking hut, and Moimango was placed in a cliffside gallery alongside other ancestors to watch over the village. But after many years out in the elements, Moimango needed some care.

Mummification was practiced for centuries in Koke, but it's a skill that's largely been forgotten. Christian missionaries have told the Anga there should be no mummifying because it's against God's law. Gemtasu requested my help in bringing this tradition back to life. When he dies, he'd like to be mummified too, so he can sit next to his father on the cliff overlooking their village.

As in treating a living patient, one of our biggest concerns is not harming the mummy. When Moimango was first brought down for me to examine, I was nervous about how he was propped up. His head was bouncing—we needed to pay attention to that right away. Normally we'd stabilize the head with a neck brace, but I realized Koke would not have access to this. Still, the Anga knew the jungle. So we created a special patch from tapa cloth. We heated thick, sticky sap from the *komaka* tree to get his skin to adhere to the scalp. We cleaned the rodent nests from his abdominal cavity and the lichens that had grown on his toes and fingers, using lime from crushed shells. Then we covered him in ritual ocher clay.

When we finished and brought Gemtasu to see his father, he touched him on the shoulder. He started crying and jumping. He took my hands. He was saying, "I'm very pleased. He's here again. Thank you." We left the village a how-to-restore manual, and when I returned this year, Moimango still looked pretty darn good. It was such a thrill to see him again. His head was stable. They'd been taking good care of him. It made me so happy to do a good job for an old man who loved his father. Science is what brought me there, but the human experience meant the most to me.

About Our Grantee

Ronald Beckett, 57, is a professor emeritus of biomedical sciences at Quinnipiac University in Connecticut. He did fieldwork in April 2010 to study mummification techniques and rituals of Papua New Guinea's Anga culture.

INSIDE GEOGRAPHIC

In a tank at a New
Zealand aquarium
an eel greets
Jennifer Hayes.

ON ASSIGNMENT Eel Appeal Inside the National Kiwi
Centre in Hokitika, New Zealand, is a two-story tank full of old
eels. How old? "About 85 to 100 years," says David Doubilet,
who documented the fish with his photographic assistant
and wife, Jennifer Hayes (above), for this issue. Doubilet and
Hayes were allowed in the tank to demonstrate the length—
about six feet—of these freshwater New Zealand longfins.
The two were told to cover up fully or risk being chomped
on. Although the eels did try to wriggle under their neoprene
hoods and face masks looking for flesh, recalls Doubilet, "they
were polite enough not to bite their guests."

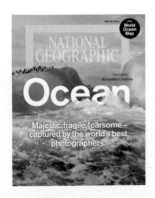

SPECIAL ISSUE
Water World
Oceans
cover nearly three-fourths of
our globe and play a role of
equal significance in Earth's
biodiversity. Our newest special
issue explains the workings of
our seas and explores ways to
improve our relationship with
them. Find *Ocean* on news-
stands September 14 or at *ngm
.com/ocean-special* ($10.99).

Society Updates

NAT GEO CHANNEL
Go on patrol with the law
officers of America's largest
state in *Alaska State Troopers*,
a weekly series beginning
September 21 at 10 p.m. on the
National Geographic Channel.

NG BOOKS
Soul of a Lion chronicles the
true story of conservationist
Marieta van der Merwe and
the imperiled wild animals she
devotes her life to in Namibia.
Look for it in bookstores
September 21 ($26).

GeoPuzzle Answers

GEOPUZZLE

Sister Dearest

Puzzle by Cathy Allis

For a long time no one knew who lay in the coffin at left, found in tomb KV55 in Egypt's Valley of the Kings. DNA tests seem to have solved the mystery, identifying the royal within as King Tut's father. For more DNA revelations, read the story on page 34—and the tinted verse in this month's GeoPuzzle.

ACROSS

1 Woody Allen pseudo-documentary
6 Feeling no pain
10 Fla. neighbor
13 Flared skirts
15 Pisa is on it
16 Card table shout
17 With 22 and 35 Across, lines 1 and 2 of an original verse about a new DNA discovery
20 Ancient Greek portico
21 Fried on both sides
22 See 17 Across
28 Kuala Lumpur native, e.g.
29 Numbered composition
30 Designer von Fürstenberg
31 Touched down
32 Prefix meaning atmosphere
35 See 17 Across
40 It makes kin kind?
41 Lapse
42 French Riviera resort
43 Grandson of Adam
44 Alternatives
47 With 53 Across, lines 3 and 4 of the verse
51 __ cloud, theoretical sphere of comets
52 Vaulted church recess
53 See 47 Across
61 We're in the Cenozoic one
62 Street-fleet member
63 Washington city near Mount Rainier
64 Caustic solution
65 Neat freak's bane
66 Full of chutzpah

DOWN

1 Drummer Starkey, Ringo's son
2 Yalie
3 Vietnam Memorial architect Maya
4 Gerund maker
5 Manages to make ends meet
6 Tears into
7 Nest egg for one's sr. years
8 Serengeti antelope
9 Darlin'
10 Plant source of tequila
11 LP jacket
12 Tennist who married Brooke, then Steffi
14 "Kama __"
18 Warner Bros. animation
19 AAA jobs
22 The __, Dutch seat of government
23 Tie the knot on the lam
24 Verbal storm
25 Blessed
26 Grand-scale tale
27 Judges' follower, or a judge Bill appointed
28 Knit, as broken bones
31 European peak
32 Friends, in Firenze
33 Roast host
34 Bar or bakery shelfload
36 "Say it __ so!"
37 Baseball's Moisés, Felipe, Matty, or Jesús
38 What a shopper may consult
39 Basic element
43 "¿Cómo __ usted?"
44 Heads: Italian
45 Brazen type
46 Like the Broadway show *Tru*
47 White sale item
48 White with old age
49 Constellation bears
50 "Sir" in colonial India
54 Those of Columbo's rank: abbr.
55 "Erie Canal" song mule
56 Losing tic-tac-toe row
57 Instrument played by Don Ho
58 Bygone Russian space station
59 Year Pope Benedict XVI was elected
60 Woo-hoo!

Answers in Inside Geographic